FORESTRY COMMISSION

Booklet No. 20

Know Your Broadleaves

Text by HERBERT L. EDLIN, B.SC.

Forestry Commission

Drawings by CHRISTINE DARTER, B.SC.

LONDON: HER MAJESTY'S STATIONERY OFFICE

1968

(Reprinted with amendments 1973)

A

PLATE I
Lombardy poplars beside the Thames.

KEY TO COVER PICTURE

Horse Chestnut   Beech

                              English
                              Elm
                              tree

Rowan   Ash

              Lime
              tree

                              Silver
                              Birch
                              tree

Hazel

Sycamore   Sessile Oak

Contents

In alphabetical order by scientific names

4

PLATE II
Aspen poplars.

Introduction

The broadleaves, or hardwood trees, are the leading feature in the British landscape of woods and hedgerows. In the past they were the country's main source of building material, fencing, and fuel. Today, when we have other sources of heat and power, and steel and concrete play so large a part in building, the hardwood timbers of these attractive trees are less important to our economy. But there is still a very substantial trade in good sound oak, beech, ash, sycamore and elm, for the better classes of furniture making and joinery, while poplar is used for matches, and willow for cricket bats.

To a growing extent, the country's needs of timber in bulk are nowadays met by the conifers, or softwood trees, which have been described in detail in the companion volume *Know Your Conifers* (Forestry Commission Booklet 15, H.M.S.O., 30p net).

Most forest planting today is done, inevitably, with these conifers. But the landscape, shade and shelter values of the broadleaves are so great that they are always likely to play the larger part in hedgerows, as street trees, and in general amenity planting. Most of them are natives, and these are firmly established in old natural, or semi-natural, woodlands throughout the British Isles.

Our broadleaved trees form part of the vast natural broadleaved forest of Northern Europe, which once stretched, almost unbroken, from the Atlantic to the steppes of Russia. Similar forests are found in eastern Asia, on the upper slopes of the Himalayas, and right across North America. The key feature of all these woods and trees is, as the name implies, the broad leaf, which is shed each autumn as the colder weather approaches.

The Leaf and its Work

Only a few of our broadleaves, such as box, holly and evergreen oak, retain their leaves through the winter months. All the rest lose them in the autumn, and pass through the coldest part of the winter with branches and twigs bare, and with their delicate shoot tips hidden within resting buds. This enables them to survive through the unfavourable period for growth, when the shoots might well be damaged by frost, by winter storms battering the leaves to fragments, or by drying out when the soil is frozen or too cold to yield its moisture. The few broadleaves which keep their leaves in winter also have protective buds, and their leaves are tough and waxy like many of the evergreen conifers to resist water loss.

The alternating leafy and leafless phases in the life of the *deciduous* tree reflect the changing seasons. In spring, as the land warms up, a new set of leaves expands from opening buds, clothing the branches with fresh, bright green foliage. All summer through these leaves carry out their essential function of absorbing and using the energy of sunlight to manufacture organic food materials by the remarkable process of *photosynthesis*. Every leaf contains within it the substance *chlorophyll*, which gives it its green colour. In sunlight, and in the presence of sufficient moisture, the chlorophyll uses the light energy to make chemical substances which can later release energy for growth, or else be used to build up the tree. Carbon dioxide, present in the air within and around the leaf, is combined with water to form energy-rich sugars. Together with mineral salts absorbed by the roots, these are transformed by intricate chemical processes into all the complex materials that make up the tree's substance—wood, roots, flowers and seeds, as well as the leaves themselves.

In autumn, the tree withdraws much of the mobile food material from its leaves, which slowly change colour from green to brown, yellow and red, or orange. Then, their work done, they fall away from a definite point of union with the twigs, leaving behind them small leaf scars. Already the tree has made preparations for a fresh crop of leaves in the ensuing spring, and the buds from which these will spring can be seen already formed, waiting for their long winter rest.

The falling leaves, drifting to the forest floor, decay to make a rich mould, still holding mineral nutrients. This leaf litter forms a fertile addition to the soil in which the trees' roots live and feed; in fact it returns to the ground the vital minerals won earlier.

A few of our broadleaved trees are *evergreen*, and their leaves have a longer cycle of life. Some of them, like the holly, are native; others come from southern Europe, or from other countries with a "Mediterranean" climate of warm moist winters. Each leaf on an evergreen broadleaf tree lasts for several years; every year new ones are added, and a few of the older ones fall, but the tree as a whole is never leafless.

6

The timber of broadleaved trees is known as *hardwood*, because in most kinds, though not in all, it is physically much harder than that of the conifers, or softwood trees. Its structure, as seen under the microscope, is very complex, and varies a great deal from one kind of tree to the next. This results in a fascinating variety of appearance and working properties, which makes certain timbers far more suitable for certain work than others. Ash, for example, makes tough axe handles, whereas elm is used for chair seats since it never splits.

How to Know the Broadleaves

All broadleaved trees belong to the great natural order of plants called the Dicotyledones, which are distinguished by having *two* seed-leaves or cotyledons in every seed. There are numerous families of these plants, many of which include both trees and smaller plants. Each family is defined, in a rather complicated way, on the basis of the structure of its flowers. This approach to naming trees, though essential for the botanist, does not help the ordinary enquirer very much. The flowers of trees are, in any event, apt to open high up in the crowns, they are only available for a few weeks each year, and—when you examine them—they often prove to be exceptional for the plant family concerned, or to be very much like those of some unrelated tree. Tree flowers are often grouped in catkins, and as a rule each catkin carries only male, or only female, flowers, which gives the investigator further problems.

A more practical approach is to learn the characters of each *genus* of trees, with the aid of a book such as this, which brings out their key features. Each plant family is made up of one or more genera, the members of which show a common pattern of bud, leaf, flower, and fruit. Each genus, in turn, consists of one or more *species*, distinguished by much smaller points of difference.

The names used for both genera and species are Latin ones, and the generic name, with a capital letter, always comes first. Thus, *Fagus sylvatica*, the common beech tree, belongs to the species *sylvatica*, within the genus called *Fagus*. These scientific names, in Latin, are used by botanists and gardeners in all the countries of the world, although the trees also have local names in each local language. Thus, beech is *Buche* in German, and *Hêtre* in French, but it is *Fagus sylvatica* wherever it may be found.

The full quotation of a scientific name, given herein only on the Contents and Index pages, requires the addition of the name of the botanist or "authority" who first published that name, along with a full description of an actual "type" specimen. "L." stands for Linnaeus, the famous Swedish botanist, also called Carl von Linné, who named many species.

As a handy working plan, the trees described in this booklet have been grouped alphabetically by their generic names, followed, again alphabetically, by the name of each species. The index on the inside back cover gives a quick reference from the English name of each tree.

Once you know the characters of the genera of trees that are grown in Britain, it is fairly easy to get to know most of the trees that grow wild in temperate Europe, Asia and North America. All our common *genera* are found in those lands, so all you have to learn are the distinguishing features of the local *species* which may be different to those we know in Britain.

Whenever possible, work with two or more features from every tree that you wish to name. Single characters, such as buds, may be much alike, but a combination of bud, leaf and fruit is unique for any of our common trees.

Key Characters of Tree Genera

To identify trees you must examine each of their features on a predetermined plan, knowing just what you are looking for. The illustrations in this booklet are designed to bring out key characters in a comparable way. Leaves, twigs, and buds on both very young and very old branches may not be true to type; look therefore at specimens from average branches of a medium age.

General Tree Form and Branch Pattern

This is shown by photographs, chosen from a larger selection because they illustrate a typical pattern of growth for each kind concerned. Individual trees vary much with age, size, and situation, yet every sort of tree shows a character peculiar to its kind. This arises in large degree from the arrangement of the buds and twigs that eventually grow out into larger branches and trunks.

Bark

This is not illustrated here, except incidentally as part of a large tree photo, but notes on the more distinctive barks will be found in each text description. Bark varies a great deal, even on the same tree, with the age and size of the twig or branch concerned. It is a great help to the experienced forester, accustomed to living with trees of all ages and sizes, but rather confusing to the beginner.

Twig and Bud

Twigs and buds are of great value for identification because they are so easily found and are so constant in design for each sort of tree. In the winter months they are the main clue to a tree's identity, and even in summer the bud pattern is easily revealed by stripping away expanded leaves. It is only hard to see during a few weeks in spring, when the leaves are expanding.

A key drawing of a typical winter twig is therefore included for every tree shown. Points to look for are:

(a) *Are the buds solitary and alternate, or are they grouped in opposite pairs?*

(b) *Are they blunt or pointed?*

(c) *Do they show, on their surface, many scales or only a few?*

(d) *Are they large or small, in relation to the twig that bears them?*

Below most buds comes a scar, left by a leaf that fell last autumn; the size and pattern of this scar often helps identification. So does the general character of the twigs, difficult to describe in words but well shown in the drawings.

Leaf

There is a wonderful variation in the structure of a leaf. The tough, dark green, leathery leaves of evergreens will at once mark them out. When you examine the softer leaf of a deciduous tree you should ask these questions:

(a) *Is it a simple, undivided leaf?*

Or one split into many lobes?

Or one divided into leaflets, that is, a compound leaf?

(b) *What is its general shape—long and slender, round and broad, or something in between?*

(c) *Is its edge toothed or smooth?*

Flower

The flowers of broadleaved trees are available only for a short spell in spring, and for most kinds it is necessary to examine both male and female ones to learn the full story. They have been shown in considerable detail in our drawings. Questions to ask when naming a tree that is in flower include these:

(a) *Are its flowers catkin-like, or do they bear large petals and sepals like most common flowering plants?*

(b) *Is the catkin examined a male one or a female one?*

Having picked out—possibly with the aid of a hand lens—the male stamens or the female pistils, you should compare them with the detailed pictures. Both the details and the general shape of the catkins help to identify each tree.

Fruit

Autumn fruits and seeds provide the most easily recognised features of every tree. For this reason they have been displayed on our front cover, as well as being shown in more detail in the text drawings. Technically, a *fruit* is the product of a single flower, and may consists of a single seed or else hold many seeds. But with many trees the feature that first strikes the eye is a fruit-cluster, or fruit-catkin, built up of the fruits of many small flowers. It is often more helpful to observe the general character of this fruit-cluster than to consider how each unit of it should be classified botanically.

Points to look for on fruit-clusters, fruits and seeds, include the following:

(a) *Are the fruits or seeds borne in groups or spaced singly and well apart?*

(b) *Are the fruits succulent, or hard and dry?*

(c) *Do the seeds bear wings, or tufts of hair, or not?*

(d) *Are the seeds large hard nuts, or small fine grains?*

(e) *What is the shape of the pod, husk, or cup that bears them?*

Remember, use more than one feature, if at all possible.

All the drawings in this booklet have been made from living material at a definite phase of growth. Nearly all of them are the work of Mrs. Christine Darter, a skilled botanical artist who has selected and verified the identity of all the plant material she has shown.

Acer campestre   Field Maple

The first genus of trees described and illustrated here is that called *Acer*, which includes both the common sycamore and the many kinds of maple. It is the major genus of a large family of trees, called the Aceraceae, and it includes a great number of species in North America and Eastern Asia. The maple trees of Canada and the United States are famous for their wonderful displays of colour in the fall of the year. One of them, the Sugar maple, *Acer saccharum,* is tapped each spring for the sweet sap that is then rising rapidly from the roots to the trunk; this is concentrated in iron pans over wood fires, out in the forest, to yield maple syrup and maple sugar; boiling must be done in a few hours, or it turns sour. One of the Japanese maples, *Acer palmatum,* is now widely grown in British gardens for its vivid displays of autumn colour; there are many named varieties of it, and the best collection of them in Britain is in the Forestry Commission's Westonbirt Arboretum, near Tetbury in Gloucestershire.

Only one kind of maple is native to Britain, that is *Acer campestre,* the field maple. Although it is a pretty tree, it is neither attractive enough to merit planting for ornament, nor big enough to yield commercial timber. We find it, as our photograph suggests, along headerows and waysides, where it provides nothing useful except shelter from sun, rain and wind. In the past its hard, smooth-textured, creamy-brown wood was often used for carving bowls, spoons and platters, while smaller stems made sturdy stakes or tool handles.

Field maple is only really common on lime-rich soils in the south and east of Britain, and particularly so on the chalk downs of the south-east. It is seldom seen on line-free soils, and it is not found at all in the north-west of Scotland. In Ireland it is native, but scarce.

The bark of the Field maple is grey-brown in colour, rough in texture, and divided into many squares by shallow fissures. The tree rarely grows taller than sixty feet, with a girth of six feet, and is often a mere bush. It branches low down, and its spreading stems end in cluster of very fine twigs, as the photo shows.

The winter twigs, seen at the centre of page 18, are straight and slender, and the buds, which are always in opposite pairs, are quite minute. They are pointed and reddish brown in colour. The leaves, seen opposite, have from three to five irregular lobes, each with its clear main vein. In summer these leaves are greyish green; in autumn they turn to gold.

Numerous clusters of flowers open in May, on short upright stalks that hold them just clear of the foliage. They are greenish-yellow in colour, and attract the bees, which do the work of cross-pollination, by their abundant supply of nectar. Although every flower might, in theory, develop both male and female organs, in actual fact this hardly ever happens. Within each cluster, some flowers develop as males, others as females.

A typical male flower, seen from above, appears on the left of the flower drawing overleaf. It has five sepals, five petals, and eight stamens, with only a hint of the undeveloped pistil at its centre. The female flower, shown in side-view on the right, has no developed stamens, but includes a large pistil with two recurved styles.

By mid-autumn, each flower cluster has ripened into a group of fruits, shown overleaf, on the right; all trace of the male flowers has gone, and in the place of each female flower there stands a fruit made up of two winged seeds. These paired winged seeds are a key feature for all the maples or *Acer* species. In Field maple they are rather flat, and the angle between the two seeds of each pair is small—often they are almost in a straight line.

The wings carry the seeds on windy days across the fields and downs until they rest in some hollow or hedgerow. There they lie dormant for eighteen months, and eventually germinate on some warm spring day. Field maple is seldom planted and it holds its own solely because it bears, and spreads, its seeds so freely. It is quick to colonise abandoned pastures and waste lands on the chalk and limestone hills.

PLATE III
Field maples flowering in May ($\times \frac{2}{3}$). Left, male flower, seen from above ($\times 3$). Right female flower side view ($\times 4$).

PLATE IV
Field maple fruiting in October ($\times \frac{2}{3}$).

PLATE V
Field maple in winter

Acer platanoides .... Norway Maple

We call this tree the Norway maple because it was first introduced from Scandinavia, but it is also common throughout Central Europe, including the foothills of the Alps. It gives us, each spring, something that no other timber tree can provide—a brave burst of blossom on bare leafless boughs. The photograph on page 14 has caught this brief spell of breathtaking beauty. These flowers are bright greenish yellow in colour; they are borne in upright clusters, as the flower picture shows, and have larger petals than is usual for a maple. A female flower is illustrated on the left, with a male flower on the right-hand side.

The winged seeds that follow in autumn have a rather sharper angle, between each pair, than have those of the Field maple. They sprout in the spring after they fall, following a six-month winter rest. Naturalised trees sometimes spring up on waste ground.

The winter buds of the Norway maple, which are shown on page 18, are small though not minute. They are warm russet-brown in colour.

Noway maple leaves have five rather shallow lobes, and each vein ends in a narrow sharp point. It is helpful to memorise this leaf design, which marks out this tree from other species of *Acer*. In spring they are a fresh emerald green, in summer pale green, while each autumn they change to a brilliant yellow, orange or crimson.

The wood of Norway maple is hard, strong and smooth-textured. Much is harvested in Europe, where it is used for furniture, wood-turning and wood-carving. But Norway maple is not planted as a timber producer in Britain, because it does not reach the useful dimensions found in the nearly-related sycamore, which has similar uses.

It is grown only as a very desirable ornamental tree, for its early flowers and its rich autumn leaf colour. Though rather large for the garden, it makes a good street or park tree that needs little pruning.

PLATE VI
Sycamore: Bole and bark characteristics; see page 15.

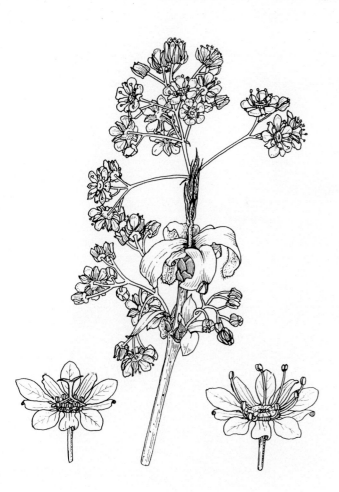

PLATE VII
Norway maple flowers in April ($\times \frac{2}{3}$). Left, female flower, ($\times 2$).
Right, male flower ($\times 2$).

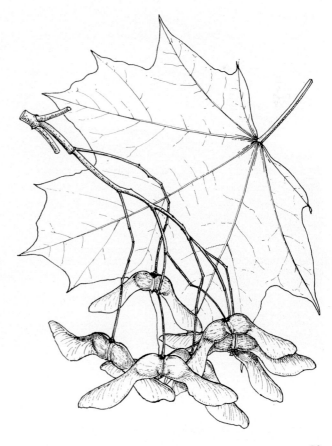

PLATE VIII
Norway maple leaf, and October fruits ($\times \frac{2}{3}$).

PLATE IX
Norway maple tree flowering in early April, before its leaves open.

Acer pseudoplatanus   Sycamore

This tree is in every respect a typical maple, but we call it "sycamore" because when it was first brought into England it was thought to be the "sycomorus" or "fig-mulberry" mentioned in the Bible. In Scotland it was thought to be a plane tree of the genus *Platanus*, and both tree and timber are still called "plane" in that country.

Sycamore is a very common forest tree in Central Europe, and grows as a native no farther away than the outskirts of Paris. But in prehistoric times it failed to spread across the Channel to England and it was unknown here until some unrecorded date in the Middle Ages. Once it had arrived, it throve and established itself firmly in our woodlands, and it now behaves just like a native tree. The well-known winged seeds enable it to spread rapidly, and as it bears heavy seed crops every year its seedlings often become a nuisance to gardeners.

Sycamore twigs, shown on page 18, are sturdy, and its buds, which are ranked in opposite pairs, are plump, with green outer scales. The leaves are large, and have lobes with rounded outlines, carrying shallow teeth. The flower-clusters, unlike those of the two other maples described, hang downwards. They are greenish-yellow in colour, and their petals are quite small. They are pretty, but not very conspicuous. Nevertheless the bees always find them, for they yield ample nectar. Certain flowers in each cluster are male and others female, while others again, near the tip, often remain sterile.

Sycamore seeds are plump, and carry wings that are narrow at the base, broader farther out. The two winged seeds are set at a sharp angle towards each other. When they fall, they usually do so as a pair, and drift down to earth spinning round like the blades of a helicopter. They sprout next spring, sending out a pair of long strap-shaped seed leaves. It is an odd feature of the sycamore that these seed-leaves are already green, before they have emerged to greet the light.

Sycamore bark, smooth at first, gradually develops rough flat surface plates that fall away from time to time, exposing younger bark below. The bark as a whole is a dull metallic grey, but fawn-coloured where freshly exposed. (Page 12).

Sycamore forms a forest tree of the first size, records for height in Britain being 112 feet, and for girth 23 feet. It is capable of living to an age of several hundred years, though most trees are felled at an age of 100 years or so for their valuable timber. When grown in the open surroundings of a park, it forms a magnificent specimen, with tier upon tier of lustrous green foliage soaring up to form a rounded dome.

The wood of sycamore is a very pale cream, almost white, in colour, with no well-marked figure or grain. It is hard and strong, and can be worked well to a very smooth finish. It enjoys a steady demand, and a good price, for furniture making and fine joinery, and it is also used by wood-turners and wood-carvers for bowls, platters, and spoons. Formerly much was used for rollers in textile mills, because it does not stain the cloth.

Figured sycamore, that is, wood showing an attractive pattern of light and dark shades in the grain of its wood, is exceptionally valuable for cutting into decorative veneers. A good mature stem showing "ripple" or "fiddle-back" figure may be worth £1,000. This high price is paid because a large area of thin veneer can be cut from a single large log.

Sycamore is in fact always used for the back of a fiddle, or any similar instrument of the violin family, and also for its sides and stock.

Good sycamore can only be grown on fertile soil, preferably one rich in lime, in well-sheltered surroundings. A good deal of commercial planting for timber is carried out on private estates where the land is known to give valuable stems. Sycamore is hardy everywhere, and some of the finest timber comes from the north of England, particularly Yorkshire.

A further use of sycamore is as a shelter tree. It is very windfirm, and it will face up to the very worst exposure, either inland or near the sea. In northern England, and also in North Wales, sycamores have often been planted to shelter the most exposed, stone-built upland farmsteads. The northernmost woodland in Britain is a plantation of sycamores on the Queen Mother's estate at the Castle of Mey, on the very exposed north coast of Caithness.

Sycamore leaves are often stained with black patches caused by the Tar-spot Fungus, *Rhytisma acerinum*, and leaves so affected can be seen in our cover picture. This

PLATE X
Sycamore flowering in May ($\times \frac{2}{3}$). Left, female flower ($\times 3$).
Right, male flower ($\times 3$).

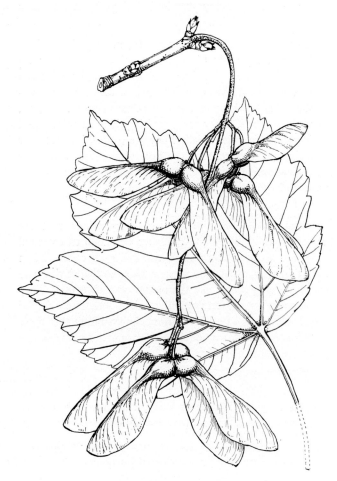

PLATE XI
Sycamore fruiting in October ($\times \frac{2}{3}$)

PLATE XII
An open-grown sycamore in summer.

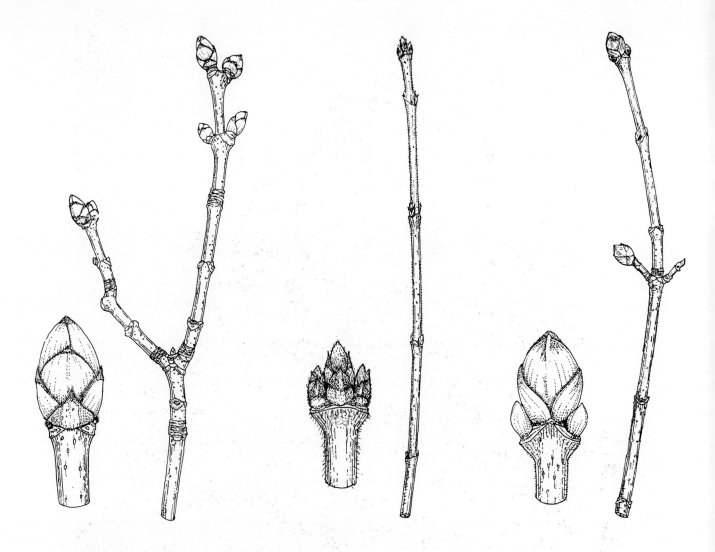

PLATE XIII
Winter twigs and buds of sycamore and maples; twigs are
two-thirds natural size; buds are three times natural size.
Left, Sycamore. Centre, Field maple. Right, Norway maple.

fungus overwinters on the leaves after they have fallen, and
the black patches produce fresh spores in the spring, which
carry the infection to a fresh crop of leaves next year.
Luckily the Tar-spot fungus causes only trivial damage to
the tree. It is never seen in cities, because it is poisoned by
the sulphur dioxide in the smoky air.

Sycamore foliage and Fruits are illustrated on the front
cover.

PLATE XIV
Sycamore seedling ($\times \frac{1}{2}$); note unlobed early leaves.

18

Aesculus hippocastanum   Horse Chestnut

This very beautiful tree was brought to Britain from the Balkans in 1616. It draws its name from its fruit, which resembles that of the Sweet chestnut tree, but all its other characters are quite distinct. The description of "Horse" chestnut springs from the fact that these nuts were fed by the Turks to ailing horses, though normally all animals refuse to touch them. Horse chestnut timber is nearly white in colour, and smooth and soft in texture. It has no real commercial use, though it is sometimes made into trays or toys. The tree is grown solely for ornament and it makes, as our photo shows, a magnificent park and avenue display. The bark is greyish brown, and as it ages it breaks up into rough squares. The trunks of old trees often become ribbed or fluted.

Horse chestnut has remarkably stout twigs, with bold oval buds set in pairs. In winter the outer bud-scales are covered with a sticky resin, which is probably a safeguard against insect attack. Below each bud there is a distinct horse-shoe shaped leaf scar, carrying a series of tiny knobs near its edge. These knobs, which resemble horse-shoe nails, are actually the scars left by the main veins of the leaf that fell in the previous autumn. People often gather these buds and place them in water indoors, so as to watch the gradual unfolding of the bright emerald green leaves. Whilst in the bud, the leaves are covered in a fawn-coloured down, which falls away as they open.

Horse chestnut leaves are compound ones, made up of several leaflets springing from a central stalk. They spread out like the fingers of a hand and this kind of compound leaf is called *palmate*. There are usually five leaflets, but sometimes only three, or as many as seven.

The flower-spikes of horse chestnut are a magnificent sight when they open in May. They are massed near the tip of the branches, and carry the white blossoms well clear of the foliage. They bear the youngest flowers towards their tips, on groups of short branched stalks. Each separate flower is strongly one-sided or *zygomorphic*, not symmetrically round as in most other trees. There are five green sepals and five white petals; the largest and boldest petals are at the top of each flower, and all of them have crinkled edges. Within the petals comes a group of 6-8 stamens, which are all curved downwards; this arrangement provides a landing point for nectar-seeking bees, and also ensures that they

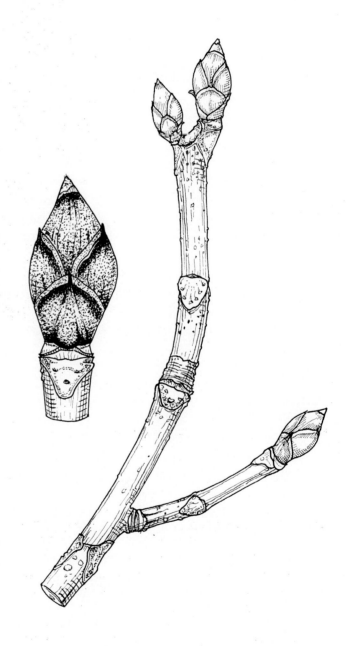

PLATE XV
Winter twigs of Horse chestnut (life size). Winter bud ($\times 3$).

PLATE XVI
Horse chestnut leaf and flower spike in May, life size.

pick up plenty of pollen to carry to the next flower. Hidden amid the stamens is a stigma on a short style, which receives pollen brought by the bees from another blossom.

After the petals have faded and fallen, the ovary at the base of the style expands rapidly to form the familiar spiky green husk. Within it, one or two large nuts develop—the well-known horse chestnuts, or "conkers." Each has a conspicuous pale brown patch on one side, but is bright chestnut brown elsewhere. Boys gather these nuts and thread them on strings for mock battles; the harder the nut the more likely it is to shatter its opponent.

Horse chestnuts are easily raised from seeds, provided the seeds are stored under moist conditions—for example in damp sand—all the winter through. The whole nut remains below ground, and sends up a stout shoot that bears compound leaves right from the outset. This tree belongs to the natural family Hippocastanaceae. The Red Horse chestnut is a hybrid, × *Aesculus carnea*, which arose by crossing with the American Red buckeye, *A. pavia*; nurserymen increase it by grafting on to a common white-flowered stock.

Fruits and leaves appear in the cover picture.

20

PLATE XVII
Horse chestnut leaf, fruit and seed, October ($\times \frac{1}{2}$).

PLATE XVIII
Horse chestnuts blossoming in a park in late May.

Alnus glutinosa

Alder

Alder is the first catkin-bearing tree to be considered in this booklet, so let us look first at these remarkable structures. The large drawing on page 24 shows fertile catkins in March; they open then, before the leaves appear, because that is the best time for the wind to carry pollen from male to female flower. The long, dangling male catkins are seen on the left, with the short, club-shaped female catkins just above them; the other structures are the winter buds from which leaves and shoots will emerge in April.

Each male catkin has a long central stalk, from which little groups of flowers, called *dichasia*, spring off at intervals. A single *dichasium* is shown, at twelve times its natural size, at the top right-hand corner of the drawing. At its foot is a stalk, while at the top you can see one large *bract*—a modified leaf, with just below it four smaller bracts, called *bracteoles*. Each of the three structures in the centre of the drawing is an individual male *flower*, consisting of four petals and four stamens, displayed like the arms of a cross. A male catkin consists of about forty dichasia, holding in all some 120 flowers with 480 stamens. Its only function is to shed clouds of yellow pollen; then it withers and falls.

The female catkin, seen enlarged to seven times its natural size at the lower right-hand corner, is a smaller and simpler structure. Each of the bracts represents a *dichasium*, and within it there are two female *flowers*, each with two stigmas; therefore, you can see four stigmas protruding from each bract. Each female flower is very simple indeed, being nothing but a single seed chamber or carpel, ending with the two stigmas that catch the wind-borne pollen.

After pollination the female catkin ripens into a woody "false-cone" that looks rather like that of a coniferous tree. Each bract gets bigger and becomes hard and woody, while within it four small *bracteoles*, not seen in the sketch, likewise get larger and harder. Below each woody, compound, cone-scale, each of the two flowers develops a single nut-like fruit, which is shown enlarged at the foot of page 23. In the same drawing you can see the ripe cones, typical leaves, and the young male catkins (on left) which will expand next spring. The cone-scales open in autumn and the fruits, each holding a single seed, fall out. Empty cones hang on the tree for several years, and make alder easy to identify.

The little seed of the alder is spread, to some degree, by the wind, but it is also carried by water, since it is light and readily floats. It will only germinate easily on damp mud, and what usually happens is that the seed is carried down a stream and left stranded on its bank. Alder is very much a riverside or lakeside tree, as the photo on page 25 shows. You can grow it as a planted tree on any reasonably moist soil, but it rarely occurs naturally away from water. Another factor that limits its spread is its dependence on another organism for much of its nourishment. Its roots develop curious ball-shaped nodules, containing a living bacterium, *Schinzia alni* Alder is only vigorous where this bacterium is found; it is common on marshy soils, but not elsewhere. Its function is to fix nitrogen from the air, and this helps alder to thrive on infertile soils.

Alder is easily identified at most times of year by its *stalked* side buds, shown on page 23. Its leaves are simple, round in shape, with shallow teeth on their edges; the notch at the tip of their main vein is a key feature for identification. Alder bark is very dark greyish brown, almost black, in colour and it becomes broken up into small squares.

Occasionally alder becomes a tall timber tree, up to ninety feet high. More often it is seen as a many-branched bush, because most alders have been cut over in the past to give a harvest of poles or small timber. The only regular use for alder wood today is in turneries; it is easily worked, but hard and strong enough for simple uses, which include broom heads and cheap tool handles. In the past much alder was used for carving into soles for clogs—these are working shoes with a wooden base and leather uppers, which carry iron runners below the sole to take the wear; they were once universally worn on farms and in mills in Lancashire and neighbouring counties.

Another major use of alder poles was to provide charcoal for gunpowder. It is better than that of most other trees, and gunpowder mills were usually sited beside alder swamps. The bark was once harvested for tanning. When it is stripped from the logs, a brilliant orange colour develops, and alder is in fact the source of many traditional textile dyes.

Alder swamps are known in England, and locally in Scotland, as *carrs*, a word derived from the old Norse word *kjarr*. In Wales they are called *gwern* and in the Highlands *fearn*. They always occupy fertile alluvial soils brought down by rivers, and, therefore, they have—with but few exceptions, been cleared and drained for agriculture. Much of our fenland was once dominated by this singular tree. Wherever alder grows beside running water, its roots play a valuable part in holding up the river banks and checking the erosion of the soil. Scarcely anyone plants it today—since there is little demand for its timber, but it is sometimes used to screen pit banks.

PLATE XIX
Stalked winter bud of alder ($\times 6$).

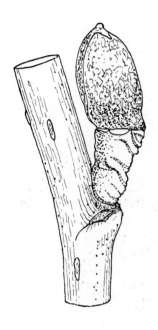

PLATE XX
Leafy twig of alder in October ($\times\frac{2}{3}$). Left, male catkins maturing for following spring. Centre, current year's female catkins, ripening to shed seed. Right, seed ($\times 8$).

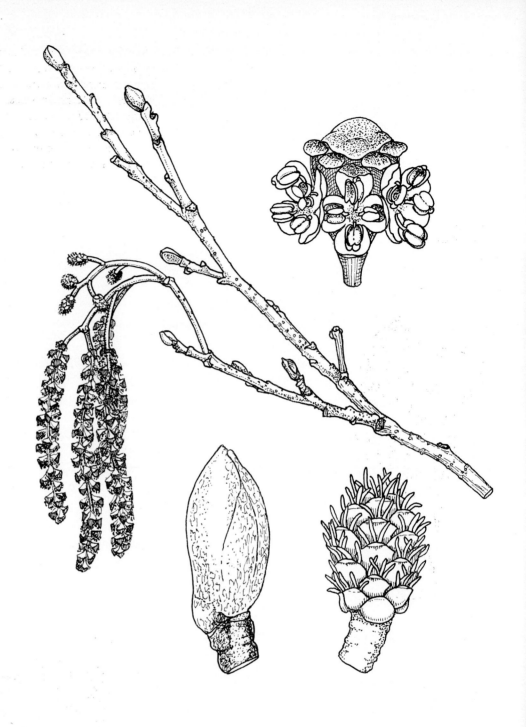

PLATE XXI
Leafless catkin-bearing twig of alder in February (life size).
Left, hanging male catkins with club-shaped female catkins just
above. Above, right, dichasium of male catkins with three
flowers (×2). Below, left, female catkin in bud (×5). Below, right,
open female catkin (×7).

PLATE XXII
Alder, typically a waterside tree, beside a Welsh lake.

Arbutus unedo   Strawberry Tree

This beautiful and unusual tree can only be found wild, in the British Isles, in the west of Ireland. It grows plentifully around Killarney and more locally as far north as Lough Gill in County Sligo. Its main home is the Mediterranean region, and it is an evergreen adapted to a climate of mild wet winters and hot dry summers. Its dark green leathery leaves, with their waxy surface, enable it to restrict water loss. They are simple in design, shaped like a long oval with toothed edges, and are borne alternately on hairy twigs.

Strawberry Tree is more likely to form a low bush than a tall tree with a single clear stem, though it can reach a height of forty feet. Its bark is reddish brown, and peels away gradually in flakes; it becomes pale grey, except where it cracks open. Strawberry tree belongs to the Heath family, or Ericaceae, and its whole aspect resembles that of a very large and woody heath plant. The flowers are bell-shaped, with five petals united into a waxy white cup, having five small green sepals at its base. They are white in colour, and fragrant, scented like lilies-of-the-valley. Within the cup

PLATE XXIII
Strawberry Tree, an evergreen, opens its flowers, and also ripens its fruit, in October. ($\times \frac{2}{3}$).

26

PLATE XXIV
Strawberry Tree.

there are ten stamens and an ovary made up of five united carpels.

These flowers open in autumn, and after they have been pollinated, and the petals have fallen away, the ovary develops into a remarkable round fruit that looks just like a strawberry. It takes a whole year to ripen through white to red, and therefore both flowers and fruit can be seen at the same time on the tree. The soft pulp of the fruit attracts birds, but people find it unpalatable, and the specific name *unedo* means "I eat one—only." At the heart of the fruit

there are many small hard seeds, which are spread by the birds that eat the berries.

Strawberry Tree is frequently planted for ornament in the south and west of England, and in coastal districts of Ireland, Scotland and Wales. It is not hardy elsewhere. The wood is hard and tough, but is too small in size for most purposes; its only recorded use is in the carving of souvenirs for tourists who visit Killarney. There are two Irish names for this fascinating tree, *caithne* and *suglair*.

Betula pendula

Silver Birch

Three species of birch tree grow wild in the British Isles and northern Europe. One is the Silver birch, also called the Warty birch because of the little warts on its otherwise smooth twigs; Hairy birch and Dwarf birch are described on page 31. All the birches have white bark, which forms as their trunks and branches expand, and later becomes gnarled and rugged with dark patches, as our cover picture and photo show. In the Silver birch it is particularly bright, with black diamond-shaped patches. The branches droop at the tips; hence the specific name *pendula*.

Birch twigs are remarkably thin and whip-like, and carry very small winter buds. The leaves have an irregular oval or diamond shape and their edges are doubly toothed. Being widely spaced along the twigs, they produce an open, airy crown that lets a great deal of light filter through. Grass, flowering plants, and even young trees can therefore thrive below a birchwood. In the Scottish Highlands many birch-woods are used as pastures and are particularly valuable because they give shelter to sheep from winter storms and snowdrifts. Foresters frequently make use of the light shelter of a thinned-out birchwood, which wards off wind, strong sunshine and hard frosts, in order to establish young crops of shade-bearing trees, such as beech, Norway spruce or Douglas firs.

Birch catkins open in April along with the leaves. The male catkins have the familiar "lambs-tail" structure of many *dichasia* set along a long drooping stalk. A single dichasium is shown, much enlarged, at the top of page 29; as in the alder, a closely related tree, it consists of three flowers, each made up of a bract, two bracteoles, and three very simple flowers. Each flower has three very small green petals and four stamens, which are forked just below the anthers. After the pollen has been shed the male catkins break up.

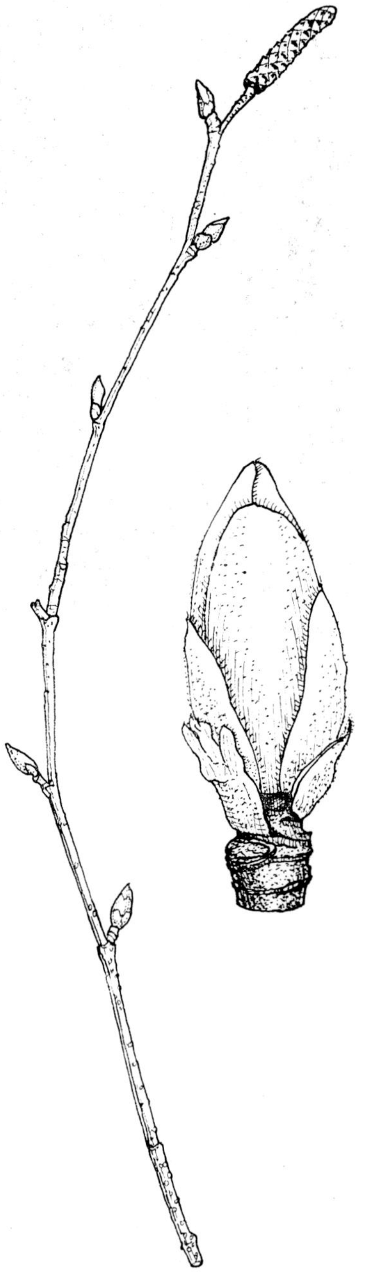

PLATE XXV
Silver birch twigs are hairless but bear tiny warts; a male catkin is shown (life size). Right, winter bud ($\times 8$).

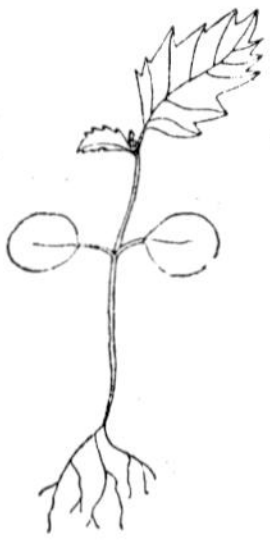

PLATE XXVI
Birch seedling ($\times \frac{1}{2}$).

28

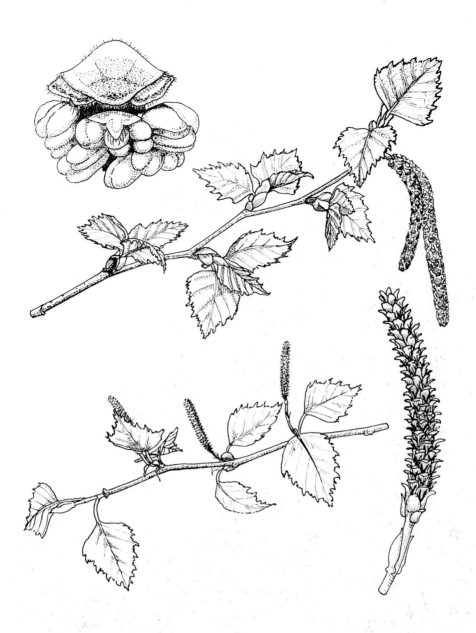

PLATE XXVII
Flowering twigs of Silver birch in April (life size). Above, male catkins, with a dichasium of three flowers (× 15). Below, female catkins, one being enlarged (× 4).

Female catkins, shown above at natural size and also enlarged, stand erect and look like bristly green caterpillars. A single dichasium from a catkin of Hairy birch is also illustrated. It is made up of a bract, two bracteoles (hidden behind the flowers) and three female flowers, each having two stigmas. During the summer these female catkins ripen to fruit catkins which eventually hang downwards in a "lambs-tail" formation that recalls the male catkins in the spring, as shown on page 34. Each separate flower has now changed into a tiny fruit, holding a single seed, with two wings to carry it through the air. At the same time the larger bracts have become curious three-lobed scales. Both fruits and bract-scales of Hairy birch differ a little from those of Silver birch, as the picture shows.

As the catkins break up in mid-autumn, both scales and seeds drift away on the wind. Seeds that alight on clear damp earth, or in rock crevices, sprout next spring. Nearly every birch tree that you see out in the woods has arisen from self-sown, wind-borne seeds. Birches for growing as ornamental trees are easily raised in a nursery, but foresters seldom plant this hardy tree for its timber.

PLATE XXVIII
Silver birch, showing its characteristic drooping habit.
Kew Gardens, Surrey.

Betula pubescens   Hairy Birch

Hairy birch can be told apart from Silver birch by its downy twigs, which lack the little warts found on those of its smooth-twigged relation. Its bark, though white, is less shiny and is more apt to peel away in strips. On the whole it is a smaller tree, with more upright branches, and its general aspect is well shown in the view of a Highland birchwood on page 33. It is a common wild tree in the north and west of Britain, where it frequently grows on damp, peaty moorlands. Its leaves have only a single series of teeth. Other fine points of difference are shown in the sketches. Bark shows grey horizontal bands.

You may of course come across individual trees that show intermediate characters; these are usually hybrids.

The timbers of both the birches are much alike, but neither is of much commercial value in Britain. In Scandinavia where trees of better form and larger size are common, the wood is widely used for furniture and for peeling the veneers that are used in birch-surfaced plywood. Our smaller trees yield a good deal of turnery wood, which is made into broom heads, tool handles, and small wooden objects of many kinds. Birch wood is pale brown in colour, with a dull surface, and is both hard and strong; it is not durable out of doors, but lasts well if kept dry. It is a first-rate firewood, and still provides most of the winter fuel for farms in Scandinavia and amid the Alps.

Many uses have been found for birch twigs, but none is important commercially today. They have been used for sweeping brooms, steeplechase jumps, and for "birching" unruly schoolboys. They make good firelighters, and also —when barked—useful whisks for beating-up sauces. Birch bark is waterproof, and sheets of it have been used for roofing woodland shelters. The tougher bark of the Canadian Paper birch, *B. papyrifera*, which can be peeled away in large sheets, is used by the Indians for making strong, light canoes.

Birches are typical "pioneer" trees, able to invade bare land and colonise it successfully. They are quick to appear without planting, wherever woods are felled and left to nature, and they readily spring up on commons where regular grazing has ceased. But birches, as trees go, are not long-lived, and the usual course of events is that they are gradually replaced by other "successor" trees, such as oaks and beeches, that have grown up in their shelter. Sixty years is a good age for a mature birch; an oak or a beech will often stand for two centuries.

Birches are often attacked by the harmful wood-rotting fungus, *Polyporus betulinus*, which bears bracket-shaped sporophones on the sides of their trunks. These brackets do not develop until the decay is far advanced, and it is then too late to save the tree—or even its timber.

Another fungus often associated with birch is the Scarlet flycap, *Amanita muscaria*. This is a bright red toadstool with white spots; it is poisonous, but luckily its appearance is so striking that it cannot be confused with mushrooms or other edible fungi. The Scarlet flycap does no harm at all to the tree, but lives in a symbiotic association with its roots; it draws certain nutrients from the tree's sap stream, and supplies others in return.

A third species of birch, not illustrated here, is found locally in the Scottish Highlands. This is the Dwarf birch *B. nana*, which seldom becomes bigger than a shrub. It is one of the world's hardiest plants, able to flourish on the tundras around the Arctic Circle. You can identify it by its small round leaves, which are edged with rounded lobes, rather than teeth, and also by its shorter, upright, and bushy branches.

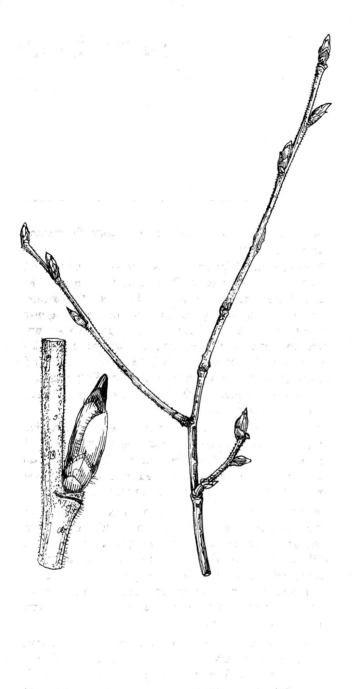

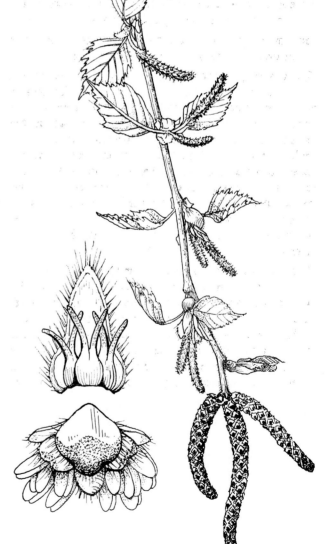

PLATE XXIX
Hairy birch twigs in winter (life size). Left, winter bud (×4).

PLATE XXX
Flowering twig of hairy birch in April, with female catkins along its sides, male catkins at its tip (life size). Left, above, dichasium of three female flowers (×20). Left, below, dichasium of three male flowers (×20).

PLATE XXXI
Hairy birches on a Scottish heath.

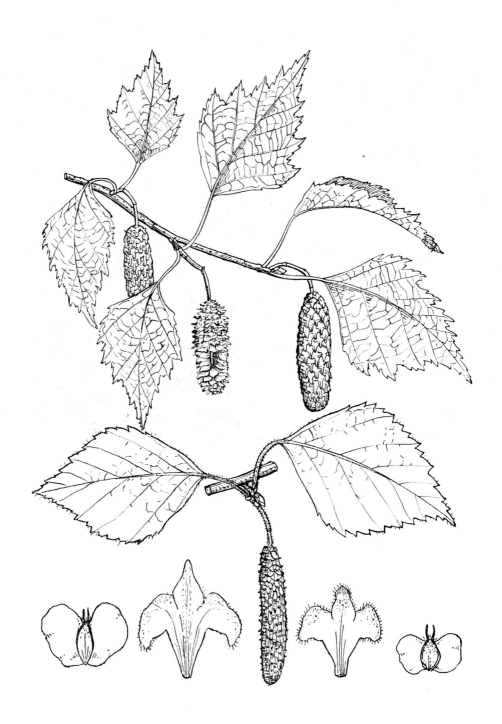

Leafy twigs, fruiting catkins, seeds and bracts of birches in
October. Above, Silver birch (life size). Centre, Hairy birch
(life size). Below left, seed and fruit bract of Silver birch ($\times 5$).
Below right, seed and fruit bract of Hairy birch ($\times 5$).

34

Buxus sempervirens

Box

Box is one of our few evergreen broadleaved trees. Its leaves, which are set in pairs along the twigs, are small and oval. Their upper surfaces are a glossy dark green, while the under surfaces are paler. The leaf texture is tough and leathery and altogether box is a very easy tree to identify by its leaf characters.

These leaves are adapted to resist water loss in dry places, and box is typically a tree of dry limestone soils. It has an extensive range from Asia Minor across Central Europe to South-east England, and is particularly common on limestone rocks in the Jura and other hill ranges of eastern France. In England it only grows wild at a very few places, all of them having lime-rich soils. The largest grove is on Box Hill, a National Trust property near Dorking in Surrey, where it grows on a very shallow soil over Chalk. It is also found on a Chalk formation near Chequers in the Chiltern Hills north-west of London, and at Box on the Cotswold Limestone of Gloucestershire. Our photograph shows a typical mature tree on Box Hill, growing as underwood below beeches; box can stand a surprising degree of shade. Its bark is pale grey, broken up into numerous small squares.

Box will only flower if it is left to grow up unclipped. The flowers are small and greenish yellow. They open in March in clusters set in the leaf axils. Each cluster holds both male and female flowers, the latter being set centrally. Each male flower consists of four green petals with four stamens set within them. The female flower also has four petals; its central ovary bears three stigmas. Box fruits, which ripen in October, are pale grey papery capsules, topped by the horn-shaded remains of stigmas. Each pod holds a large number of small hard black seeds, which gradually escape and become scattered through the woods. Natural seedlings can often be found on Box Hill; their first pair of seed-leaves are deciduous, but all later leaves are evergreen. In cultivation, box is usually seen as a low shrub, kept closely clipped to form a pleasing, neat, dense evergreen hedge or border. The dwarf strain used for this purpose is increased by dividing the clumps, so that each segment holds a group of roots.

Larger box bushes are often trained into artificial shapes, by the art of topiary. You can train a box bush into the form of a globe, a bench, or even a peacock. Box stands up to this treatment because it shoots again readily after clipping; since its leaves stand deep shade they continue to flourish very close to one another, so forming a dense wall of green foliage.

The wood of box is the hardest and heaviest that can be grown in Britain. But our few woods are so small and precious that none is harvested here; the small amount needed is imported from Turkey. Boxwood is bright orange-brown in colour, and can be polished to give a very smooth and attractive surface. It is used for rulers and drawing instruments that must be exact in size, and carry neat and accurate scales. Woodcarvers use it for the very finest artistic sculpture. It is also used by artists to make *wood engravings*, which differ from ordinary *woodcuts* in their far finer texture and much longer wear. In wood engraving the artist uses very fine and sharp tools to cut his design on the *end-grain* of a piece of boxwood. End-grain is the surface that is seen on a cross-section of a log, and as the stems of box are so small, a number of them have to be built up into a composite wood block before any sizeable picture can be engraved. This exacting technique was used for many of the cover pictures of the Forestry Commission's guide books, which were both drawn and engraved by Mr. George Mackley. The process was first developed by Thomas Bewick, the Northumbrian artist and naturalist, about the year 1800.

The largest box trees recorded in England have reached heights of thirty feet, with trunk two feet round.

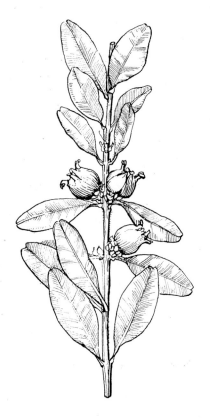

PLATE XXXIII
Flowering branch of evergreen box in May (life size). Below, left, male flower ($\times 12$). Below, right, female flower ($\times 12$).

PLATE XXXIV
Fruiting branch of box in October, showing seed capsules (life size).

PLATE XXXV
Box seedling ($\times \frac{1}{2}$).

36

PLATE XXXVI
Box tree on Box Hill in Surrey.

Carpinus betulus   Hornbeam

At first sight the hornbeam is usually mistaken for the much commoner beech, which it resembles in form, bark, and leaf. Our drawings bring out the main points of difference; for comparison, beech will be found on pages 48 to 52. Hornbeam leaves, shown on page 39, are simple and oval like those of beech, but have distinctly toothed edges, and a much stronger pattern of parallel veins. The bark, though smooth and grey as in beech, has a remarkable network of smooth metallic-blue striations, seen on no other tree. Winter buds, though beech-like, are much shorter, and are inclined inward towards the twigs, instead of pointing outwards. The flowers and seeds differ markedly from those of beech, and show the hornbeam's close relationship to the birch tree, with which it is grouped in the family Betulaceae.

The male catkins are not seen until late April, when they emerge from the buds and droop downwards. Each is made up of many dichasia, or short branches each bearing a large bract and a cluster of twelve stamens. Each stamen-group is really three flowers, consisting of four stamens apiece; each stamen is forked just below the anthers. The male catkins fall as soon as their pollen is shed.

Female catkins are grouped, as our drawing shows, close to the tips of the twigs; they look rather like shoot buds. Each female dichasium consists of a long, slender pointed bract; at the base of this are set two flowers, each with two long styles, and six tiny bracteoles. As the fruits develop, the large bract disappears, but the little bracteoles enlarge enormously and form curious, papery, pale green wings. As there are three bracteoles to each flower, the result is a pair of fruits, each with a wing composed of three fused arms. A single flower with its wing, having one long lobe and two shorter ones, is seen on page 39 (bottom left), but the usual pattern is for the flowers to be paired, as in the main drawing.

The fruit of each flower is a one-seeded nut; though this looks small to us it makes a good morsel for a hungry bird, and flocks of finches and tits frequent hornbeam trees in autumn to eat the seeds; squirrels and wood mice relish them too. Those seeds that escape attack are carried away by the wind, supported on their three-pointed wings. They lie dormant on the forest floor for eighteen months before they sprout.

38

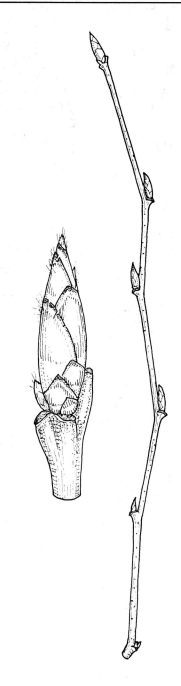

PLATE XXXVII
Winter twig of hornbeam; note how the buds hug the twigs (life size). Left, a single bud.   (×5).

PLATE XXXVIII
Flowering twig of hornbeam in late April, just as the leaves
open (life size). The drooping male catkins are made up of many
dichasia or flower groups. Top centre, one dichasium, which is
technically three flowers, is seen to consist of one bract and twelve
stamens. Female catkins are seen near tip of twig; a single one,
(× 3) appears at top left. Bottom right, one female dichasium,
seen from within (× 10) holds two flowers, with two long styles
apiece, and six bracteoles.

PLATE XXXIX
Fruiting twig of hornbeam in October, showing typical leaves.
(× ⅔). Each pair of fruits, holding two nuts attached to two
three-lobed wings, arises from one dichasium. A single nut and
its bract are shown at bottom left.

PLATE XL
A much-branched hornbeam, formerly pollarded about nine
feet up, in an Essex hedgerow.

Hornbeam is native only to the south-east of Britain, having apparently arrived too late to spread farther. You can find it in Kent and Sussex, along all the valleys of the Thames and its tributaries, and very locally in South Wales and a few other westerly districts. Elsewhere it is only seen as a planted tree. It yields a first-rate firewood, and in the past it was often cultivated in south-eastern England by the *coppice* or *pollard* methods that enabled repeated crops of poles to be cut without replanting. Our photo shows a typical pollarded tree, which was formerly lopped at head height; a cluster of branches then sprang out, after each lopping, safely above the reach of browsing cattle and sheep. Pollard hornbeams are frequent in Epping Forest and Enfield Chase, north of London. In Kent the crop was usually coppiced, that is, cut at ground level.

Left to itself, hornbeam forms a grand timber tree, up to ninety feet tall. It is also very good for hedging; a hornbeam hedge holds its fawn-coloured faded leaves on the twigs all the winter through, so providing colour and shelter.

The wood of hornbeams is exceptionally hard and strong. This explains its name, which is an Anglo-Saxon one meaning "horny (wooded) tree." It was used in the past for ox-yokes, fitting across their shoulders so that they could draw heavy ploughs or carts. It was also employed to make cog wheels for watermills and windmills, as it wears smoothly for a very long time. For the same reason, it is still used in piano mechanisms. Today its main use is in chopping blocks in butchers' shops, since it stands hard abrasive wear better than any other timber. But little hard timber — or firewood — is needed today, and hornbeam is now only planted for ornament.

Castanea sativa

Sweet Chestnut

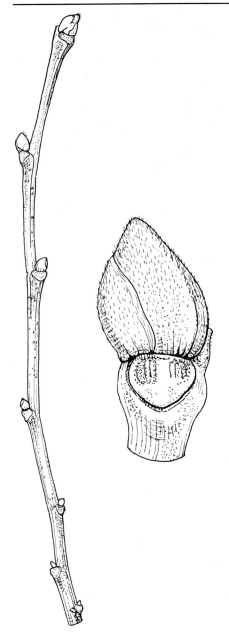

The Romans introduced this remarkable Italian tree to Britain during their long spell of dominion and colonisation, from A.D. 42 to A.D. 410; their object was to raise the familiar nuts which were, in Italy, a staple food for their legionaries. But the British climate does not encourage a good chestnut harvest, and nearly all the nuts we eat today are imported. In the south of England, the chestnut ripens fertile seeds, and it has sprung up here and there in the woods, ever since Roman times. From the Midlands northwards, chestnut is only seen as an ornamental specimen tree, artificially sown and planted.

In winter, chestnut is fairly easily known by its stout twigs, which are rather angular and marked by ridges; the winter buds are large and plump, and pinkish brown in colour. In summer the very large long-oval leaf makes recognition easy; leaves are often nine inches long by two inches broad, and glossy green above; their veins are distinct, and each side-vein ends in a sharp tooth: Chestnut bark is boldly marked by a network of ribs, often in a spiral pattern.

PLATE XLI
Winter twig of Sweet chestnut (life size); winter bud ($\times$ 6).

PLATE XLII
Fruiting branch of Sweet chestnut in October. Each spiny husk consists of a group of four bracts, enclosing up to three single-seeded fruits—the chestnuts ($\times \frac{2}{3}$).

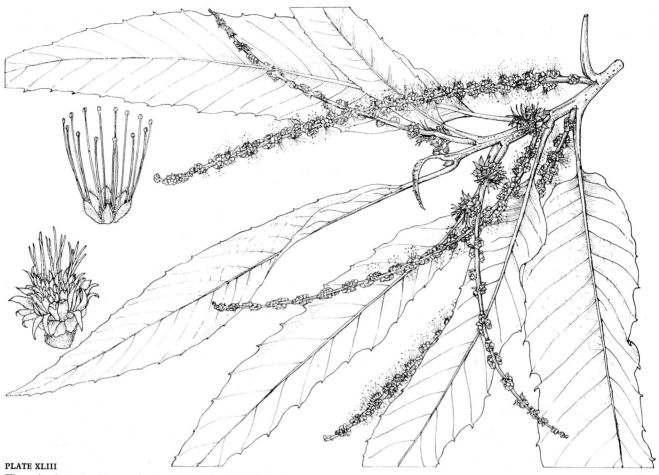

Flowering branch of Sweet chestnut in July (x 1). Each slender catkin carries many groups of male flowers; a single male flower is seen above left (× 3). Clusters of female flowers arise near the base of certain catkins; a single cluster, seen on the left, consists of many leafy bracts and three (hidden) flowers, with tufts of styles protruding (× 2). Note the large simple, toothed, leaves.

Chestnut catkins do not open until July. They are remarkable in having, as a rule, both male and female flowers on the same stalk, and also in being pollinated by insects, rather than by wind. Each catkin stalk, which is often five inches long and looks rather like a hairy caterpillar, carries numerous male flowers, bunched in groups of seven. Each male flower consists of six green petals and about a dozen stamens, with conspicuous golden anthers. Once the pollen has been shed the wholly male catkins fade and fall; the male part of a mixed catkin, however, remains attached to the base, until the fruit has ripened, and then falls with that. Female flowers appear near the base of some, although not all, of the catkins, in little groups that look like leafy buds, they are surrounded by green bracts which form a *cupule*. Usually there are three flowers in each cupule, and each is tipped with a tuft of styles. Chestnuts ripen rapidly, and in September, two months after flowering, each flower-group has changed into a fruit-group holding from one to three single-seeded nuts, the familiar chestnuts. By this time, too, the bracts forming the cupule have expanded to form a tough husk, bearing many sharp greenish-yellow spines

on the outer surfaces of distinct lobes, usually four in number.

Sweet chestnut is easily raised from seed, provided the nuts are carefully stored and not allowed to get too dry or become mouldy; moist sand is a good storage medium. Chestnut timber is very strong and its heartwood is naturally durable; it resembles oak but lacks that tree's decorative "silver grain." Trees may reach 115 feet tall, and 40 feet round. But chestnut is rarely planted to yield timber because some—though by no means all—of its trunks develop serious cracks called "shakes," which makes it hard to cut large planks from them.

In south-east England much chestnut is grown on the coppice system, to provide small poles. The woods are cut over every twelve years or so, and a fresh cluster of poles then springs out from the stump without further care or replanting. Most of the poles are cleft, always by hand—into smaller *pales* which are bound with wire to make chestnut pale fencing. Each pale contains—for its thin cross-section, a great deal of heartwood, and it is therefore both very strong and remarkably durable.

42

PLATE XLIV
A fine open-grown Sweet chestnut, ripening abundant fruits in
September.

Corylus avellana   Hazel

Hazel branches so often and so low down that it is more likely to rank as a bush than as a tree; its typical form is shown in the photo on page 48. But it is very important in British forestry because at one time very extensive coppices, or copses, of hazel were cultivated in many districts to provide small poles. Their management was simple. Every seven years or so the poles were cut; then the stump sent up fresh shoots. One seventh of the wood was cut each year, so that there was always a fresh supply ready every season. The main uses of these poles, produced so cheaply and abundantly, were as firewood, and in fencing and hurdle making. Other uses were as hedge stakes and hedging rods, bean rods, pea-sticks, clothes props, walking sticks, thatching spars for holding straw thatch on corn-ricks and house-roofs, hoops for barrels, rough baskets, and fish traps. In fact, whenever a countryman wanted "a bit of wood," he could usually get it from his hazel copse. Hazel even provided the wattles for "wattle and daub" house building.

In 1905 there were about 500,000 acres of hazel coppice in Great Britain, but by 1965 this figure had fallen to 94,000 acres, and it is still going down. The reason is the simple one that hazel poles have lost nearly all their markets to other materials. People nowadays use coal, oil, gas, or electricity instead of wood fuel, even in country districts, and wire is used for most of the fencing jobs. Here and there you may still find a craftsman making hurdles, or cutting hedge stakes or thatch spars, but you are far more likely to see a forester busy converting hazel coppices to some more profitable timber crop. Scattered woods and lines of hazel bushes still persist on patches of rough ground, not worth reclaiming for farm or forest, and they are particularly frequent in the south of England. They provide cover for

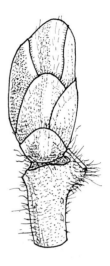

PLATE XLV
Leaf bud and hairy twig of hazel ($\times$ 7).

song-birds and game birds, and form an excellent habitat for many of our most attractive spring flowers—bluebells, windflowers, primroses and the bright pink campion.

The winter twig of hazel is typically hairy, as our sketch shows, and it bears alternate buds that are pale green in colour. Its catkins open early before the leaves appear. February is the usual month, though in mild winters you may find them in January. The male catkins, which have been visible as long buds ever since Autumn, open and reveal their characteristic "lambs-tail" outline. Each catkin consists of a series of bracts, each of which has two small bracteoles and a single flower. There are four stamens in each male flower, but their stalks are so deeply forked that on first sight there appear to be eight. These "lambs-tail" catkins fall in March, after their wind-dispersed pollen has been shed.

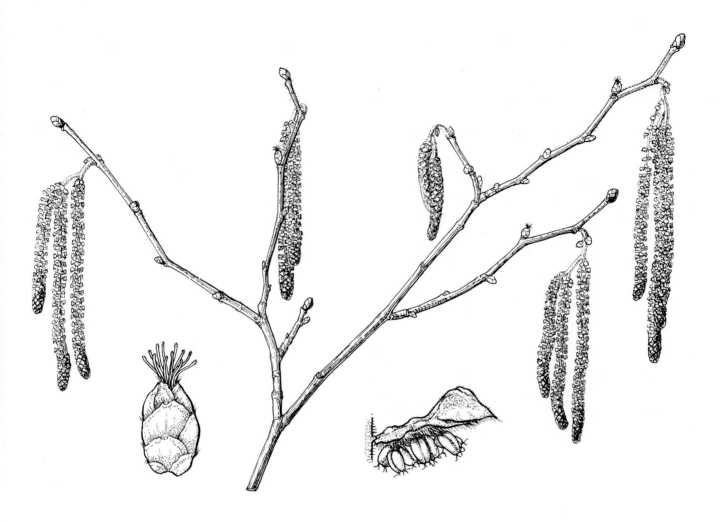

PLATE XLVI
Leafless, catkin-bearing twig of hazel in February ($\times \frac{2}{3}$). Male
catkins hang down like lambs tails; bud-like female catkins can
only be identified by styles protruding beyond their bracts.
Below, left, single female catkin ($\times$ 4), holding six female flowers,
each with two styles. Below, right, single male flower ($\times$ 12)
consisting of a bract with eight divided stamens.

45

The female catkins look very much like buds, but can be distinguished by the tuft of crimson styles that appears at the tip of each. Each catkin holds three well-developed *bracts*, and each bract carries two female flowers, each with two styles. There are therefore twelve styles protruding from each catkin, to catch the pollen from the male flowers. After pollination, both the enclosing bud scales and the main bracts wither away, but two small *bracteoles*, which are not visible at flowering time, develop from the base of each flower. They enlarge enormously into leafy structures that surround the ripening fruit, a one-seeded nut. This nut, the hard-shelled "cob nut," ripens in autumn, turning from green to brown. It is very nutritious and attracts birds, mice, squirrels and small boys, all of whom help to spread the seed. Hazel is easily raised from nuts stored under moist conditions until spring.

The cob nuts used for eating, and in cakes and chocolate, are gathered from hazel bushes grown under open conditions to give these branches ample sunlight; they are treated as orchard bushes and are pruned regularly. Most of the nuts are imported, but a few are grown in Kent. Filberts, with a longer leafy husk, are a cultivated strain of the related Balkan hazel, *Corylus maxima*. A purple-leaved hazel, *C. maxima* variety *purpurea*, is occasionally grown for ornament in gardens.

Hazel leaves open late in April, after the catkins have dispersed their pollen through the leafless woods. These leaves are very broad, and have distinct veins and a toothed edge; they taper to a short point at the tip. They are placed, like the buds, alternately along the twigs. The bark is smooth, and somewhat greenish brown, with prominent breathing pores or lenticels.

Leaves and nuts appear on the front cover.

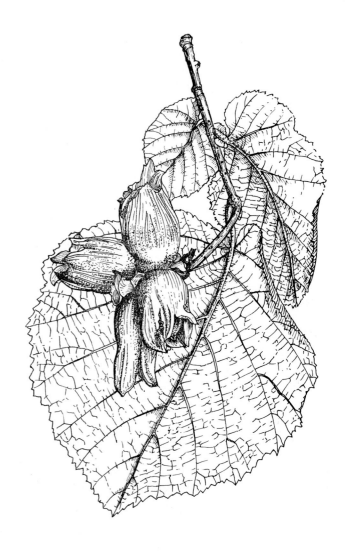

PLATE XLVII
Leaf-bearing twig of hazel in October, showing ripe nuts enclosed in leafy cupules ($\times \frac{2}{3}$).

PLATE XLVIII
Hazel usually forms a much branched bush; fresh shoots
spring up on the same pattern after each cutting of a coppice
crop.

Fagus sylvatica Beech

Beech is one of our most distinctive and handsome trees, and also an important timber producer. It is very easy to recognise, for only one other tree, the hornbeam, is at all like it. Beech buds are very long and slender, with pointed brown scales and sharp tips; they are set alternately at the angles of the rather zig-zag twigs. These twigs are rather hairy, as our sketch shows. The bark of a beech tree, even when it has reached great age and size, is nearly always smooth, and it is a characteristic metallic grey colour. Its smoothness tempts people to carve their initials on it, which gives unsightly results though it rarely harms the tree below. Nuts and leaves appear on our cover.

Our photographs show that beech can vary considerably in form. The tall tree in the woodland (p. 51) grew up as one of a group, and in its struggle for light it formed a long, upright trunk, shedding its lower side branches as they became overshaded. Its form will attract a timber merchant, though he will have to fell it with great care, as it has forked at the top; if one arm of the fork strikes the ground before the other, the whole stem may be split and so ruined. By contrast, the open-grown beech tree in the park (p. 52) has been allowed to spread its branches as far out as it wished; it may even have been topped or "pollarded" to discourage upward growth. Such a broadly-spreading beech is very picturesque, and gives much shade and shelter, but its short bole is useless as timber.

Beech leaves have a simple oval shape, with clearly-marked parallel veins. Their edges are slightly wavy. When they first open they are slightly hairy, and a pair of leafy stipules is seen at the base of each leaf; later the stipules fall away and the hairs become indistinct. Beech leaves are glossy dark green above, and paler below; they turn to bright

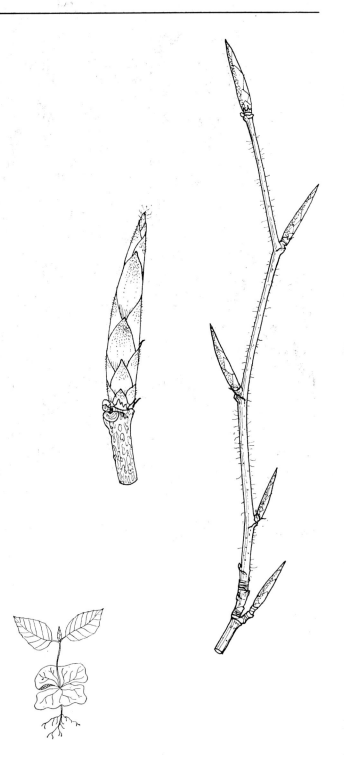

PLATE XLIX
Winter twig and buds of beech (life size). Left, a single pointed bud, with its papery brown scales, enlarged ($\times$ 2½).

PLATE L
Beech seedling ($\times$ ½).

48

PLATE LI

Flowering twig of beech in May, showing newly-opened leaves and stipules (life size). Male catkins, which hang down, hold numerous male flowers like that seen lower left (× 6). A hairy female catkin, standing upright, is seen in the centre, complete with bracts. Lower right, female catkin with all bracts removed, showing two flowers, each having three styles.

orange and brown shades before they fall in autumn. Fallen leaves persist on the forest floor for many months before they decay to form a rich brown leaf-mould. On young beech trees, and along beech hedges, faded leaves hang on right through the winter, and do not fall until spring; this makes beech hedges both attractive and valuable for shelter.

Beech catkins open in May, just after the leaves have expanded. The flowers of each sex are grouped in separate catkins on the same twig. Male catkins hang downwards on long stalks, and look like little tassels of golden stamens. Closer examination shows that each catkin has a few scales at the base of each cluster, and then a group of about twelve male flowers. Each male flower, as shown in the sketch, consists of about six hairy bracts united at the base into a cup, and about ten long stamens. Male catkins fall when their pollen is shed.

Female catkins stand erect, on shorter stalks, and have the general form of a hairy cup. This bears four hairy bracts, and a very large number of smaller hairs, which possibly represent bracteoles. When all these structures are stripped away, as in the enlarged sketch, two flowers are exposed at the centre; each has a basal ovary and three distinct styles, crimson in colour. Each flower is capable of ripening three nuts, though often only one or two mature.

Beech nuts ripen in October. By then each stalk has become longer and stouter, and the four bracts have enlarged to form a hairy cupule enclosing the seeds. Each seed is triangular in cross-section and has a hard brown husk, with a soft white kernel within. It is unusual for all the seeds to ripen and to be well-filled; in some years most of the seeds prove, on opening, to be nothing more than empty husks. Good seed crops, or "masts" occur only every four or five years. These exceptional crops are so heavy that a high proportion of the seed escapes being eaten by the numerous creatures that relish it, including squirrels, mice, pigs, pigeons, pheasants, rooks and jays. The seed lies dormant on the forest floor through the winter; it is easily stored under slightly moist conditions. After a good mast, seedlings are plentiful on the forest floor, though only a small number survive.

A beech seedling has two broad fleshy seed-leaves or cotyledons, carried on a short stalk above the soil. They look quite unlike the normal foliage leaves, which follow a few weeks later.

More beech is planted today than any other broadleaved tree. In a typical year, the Forestry Commission sets out 1,300,000 young beeches on about 800 acres of land, and there is also extensive planting on privately owned estates. The main reason is that beech is the most profitable tree of any kind, broadleaved or conifer, for people to grow on chalk or limestone hills. It also thrives well on any other reasonably fertile light soil, whether it be sand or loam, anywhere on our southern hills or northern lowlands, provided drainage is good. Small trees, removed from the crop as thinnings, are only suitable for firewood or turnery, but the larger trees harvested later have a wide range of uses.

Beechwood, which is pale brown in colour, marked by many small dark brown flecks, is hard and strong, and can readily be worked in any direction. It is widely used in furniture, and joinery, as flooring blocks, and for many small objects that need a sturdy "piece of wood." These include bowls, platters, wooden spoons, plane blocks, mallet heads, brush backs, parts of pianos, and simple hand tools. Beechwood veneers are made up into plywood for chair-making and shop-fitting. Beechwood bent to curved shapes, after treatment with hot steam, is used in "bentwood" furniture.

Beech has been widely planted throughout the British Isles, and there are few estates without a beech wood or shelter-belt. The finest stands are found in the south, particularly on the limestone Cotswold Hills around Bath, and on the chalk ranges of the Chilterns, the North and South Downs, and the Downs of Hampshire, Wiltshire and Dorset. Young beeches are easily raised from seed and established in the forest. They benefit greatly from shelter against strong sun and frost when young, so they are often established in the light shade of birch or hazel coppice.

The Copper and Purple beeches are selections made by nurserymen from a purple-leaved form, *F. sylvatica atropunicea*, first cultivated in Germany in the eighteenth century. Many of these are raised as seedlings, but the deepest coloured, like the cultivar "River's Purple", are grafted. Their green colour is masked by their copper or purple tints, which make them handsome and unusual landscape features.

PLATE LII
Fruiting twig of beech in October, showing the stalked hairy cupules that arise from each female catkin ($\times \frac{2}{3}$). Above, the four arms of the cupule open to reveal triangular nuts within.

50

PLATE LIII

A fine beech that has grown up with others in close woodland.
Note the good length of timber bole, without branches; though
the tree has forked, it still holds valuable timber.

PLATE LIV
A grand open-grown beech displaying its much branched crown
in a Scottish park.

52

Fraxinus excelsior

Ash

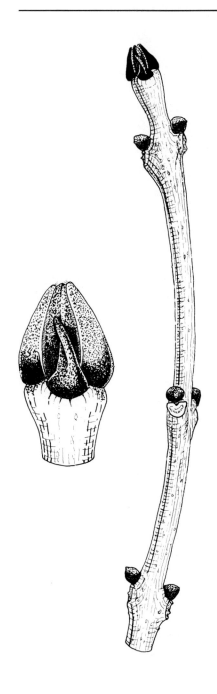

In winter the ash is very easily known by its hard black buds which are arranged in opposite pairs. The twigs, as our sketch shows, are flattened at each joint where the buds are set, and this flattening takes place alternately in two planes. The bark of ash is a characteristic pale grey; smooth at first, it becomes regularly ridged and furrowed as each stem grows stouter and older.

Ash leaves, illustrated on page 55, are remarkably large and are pinnately compound. This means that they consist of several separate leaflets, set in pairs along opposite sides of a central stalk, which ends in a solitary terminal leaflet. The number of leaflets varies, but is commonly seven, nine, eleven, or thirteen; their edges bear shallow teeth. The seedling has a very different appearance, for it starts life by bearing two oval seed leaves, which are followed by two larger, pointed-oval true leaves; the leaves of the next pair have only three leaflets each, but succeeding ones grow steadily larger, with more numerous leaflets.

The flowers of ash open in April, before the leaves expand. They are catkin-like in structure, although the ash is not closely related to other common catkin-bearing trees. As our drawing shows, the flower clusters may be dense with short stalks to each flower, or more lax and open. Each individual flower is very small, and has no apparent sepals or petals. Many flowers are all-male, and consist of nothing more than a pair of stamens. Others are hermaphrodite, with both male stamens and a female pistil, while others again are all-female, and lack stamens. Each tree may bear flowers of one type, or of two or three kinds together.

After fertilisation by the wind, the pistils ripen rapidly through the summer, and by October each female or hermaphrodite flower-cluster has expanded into the familiar bunch of ash "keys." Ash fruits are so-called because each seed, with its attached wing, has the outline of an old-fashioned key used for opening doors or chests. At first the seeds are grown, and if gathered at that stage and sown at once, they will sprout without delay. If they are left to ripen they change to brown in colour, and become

PLATE LV
Winter twigs and buds of ash (life size). Left, a single terminal bud, showing the hard black scales (× 3).

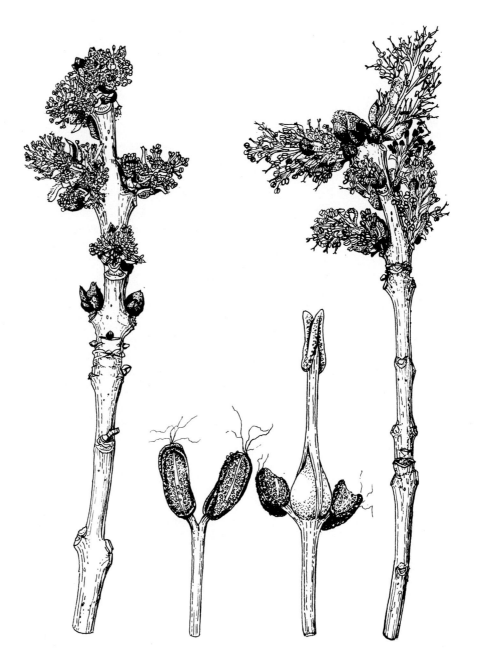

PLATE LVI
Flowering twigs of ash in April (life size); on left, a dense group
of male inflorescences; on the right, a lax inflorescence that
includes both male and hermaphrodite flowers. Centre, left, a
male flower with well-developed stamens; centre, right, a
hermaphrodite flower with two small stamens and a central
pistil ($\times$ 12).

PLATE LVII
Ash seedling ($\times \frac{1}{2}$).

54

PLATE LVIII
A cluster of ash fruits, or "keys", ripening in October. Each fruit consists of a single winged seed. A compound leaf is seen behind (all × ⅔).

dormant. This means that if they are sown later they will not germinate until eighteen months after they first ripened. In practice the forester mixes his ripe ash seed with damp sand and stores it in a well-drained pit, out of reach of birds, mice and squirrels, until the time for spring sowing comes round, eighteen months after storage began.

Ash forms a tall upstanding tree with a wide-spreading crown because the side-buds are set in opposite pairs, the branches are very apt to fork; in fact they do so whenever anything happens to the terminal bud. Ash comes into leaf late, seldom before May, and it loses its leaves earlier in October than do most other trees. These points make it a poor shelterbelt tree, though it is very hardy and can thrive far up the hills It likes a rich soil and grows best on deep loams over limestones.

The timber of ash is easily distinguished by its well-marked annual rings. Each ring has a thin band of open spring-wood pores, and outside this comes another band—thick or thin—of hard dense summerwood tissue. When ash grows *fast* it forms a broad summerwood band, and is then exceptionally strong.

Ash is the toughest of our native timbers, so it is chosen wherever there is need to absorb a hard blow or shock with out splintering. It is used for the stronger handles, including those for hammers, axes, spades and pick axes. Sportsmen use it for hockey sticks and oars, and the rims of wooden cart wheels are always made up of ash felloes. Ash is widely used in furniture, because of its strength and attractive grain, and also because it can easily be bent to curved outlines. Our cover shows leaves and fruits.

PLATE LIX
A magnificent open-grown ash tree, seen in autumn;
the tufty character of the foliage is due to heavy fruiting.

Ilex aquifolium

Holly

Holly is one of our few evergreen broadleaved trees. Its leaves are tough and leathery and are coated with wax which restricts loss of water. This may appear odd for a tree that grows in a damp climate, but in winter when the ground is frozen the holly's roots cannot obtain any water from the soil. If water was then transpired from the leaves, as would happen in a broadleaved tree with ordinary soft leaves, the holly would die of drought. This does not happen, but all the same the holly grows far more vigorously in the west of Britain, from Scotland south through Lancashire and Wales to Cornwall, than it does in the east, where the winters are harder. Native throughout the British Isles, it enjoys the mild winter climate of Ireland.

As the holly's leaves are one of the few green foods available to cattle, sheep, and deer when snow covers the ground, they are very liable to be attacked. Therefore they carry very sharp spines at the tip of each vein, for protection. Leaves on the upper branches, above the reach of browsing animals, are often spineless. There are some cultivated strains of holly that lack spines completely, and others, such as "hedgehog holly," that are very spiny indeed. Holly leaves are always wavy, and darker green above than below; they are quite soft when they first open.

Each individual leaf lives for only two or three years. Most leaves fall in spring, still green in colour, and a layer of hard, brown, old withered leaves can often be found below a holly tree. Leaves and buds are always placed alternately along the twigs, which have greenish-grey bark.

Most holly trees are either wholly male or wholly female and this explains why some hollies never bear berries. Holly flowers are grouped in bunches near the base of the leaves. They open in May and are pretty, though short-lived. As our sketch shows, there are no visible sepals, and only four petals, white in colour with purple tips and waxy in texture. At the base of the petals there are nectaries to attract the pollinating bees.

Male flowers have four well-developed stamens, but no pistil. Each female flower has four rudimentary stamens and a large pistil which later becomes a berry. The stigma, which is very short, is four-lobed; below it there is a four-celled ovary holding four seeds.

The familiar scarlet holly berries are much more plentiful in some seasons than in others. A warm, dry, sunny summer enables the trees to store up food reserves, but these are not applied to producing berries in the following autumn; instead they are used for forming the flower buds that will develop into berries *a whole year later*. The hard white seeds are scattered by berry-eating birds; if a bird eats the berry and voids the seeds they grow next spring; otherwise they lie dormant for a year.

Holly is often trimmed and trained as a hedge or an ornamental shrub. Left to itself it forms a sturdy tree with a characteristic smooth grey bark. It grows slowly and lays

PLATE LX
Flowering branch of holly in May (life size). Note soft young leaves at tip, and wavy outline of sharp, spined, evergreen mature leaves. Below, left, female flower with four-lobed pistil and rudimentary stamens, ($\times$ 5). Below, right, male flower with four fully developed stamens but no pistil.

PLATE LXI
Fruiting branch of holly in December ($\times \frac{2}{3}$).

PLATE LXII
Holly tree.

down exceptionally hard and heavy wood—smooth in texture and pale creamy-white in colour, with a faint greenish tinge.

This wood was formerly used for carving, and it still finds occasional employment in walking sticks. But most holly wood is burnt as firewood; it has very high heating power, while its water content is so low that it will burn as soon as it is felled, without any seasoning. The waxy foliage is very inflammable, even when green, and a holly tree caught by a forest fire blazes furiously.

Holly can endure deep shade, and often grows as an under-shrub below taller trees. Occasionally it grows very tall, up to seventy feet, and it can also grow to a considerable girth, eight feet or more round. When a holly seed sprouts, its first seed leaves are quite soft, and not evergreen. Natural seedlings can often be found in woods and along hedgerows.

Juglans regia

Walnut

The Romans introduced the walnut, as a cultivated nut tree, from Asia Minor to Italy and Western Europe generally, and possibly to Britain too. Its name is an Anglo-Saxon one, meaning "foreign nut," and the alternative form of "welshnut," with the same meaning, is still used in the West Country. Most walnuts you see are planted in orchards or gardens, but now and then birds drop nuts along the hedgerows, and self-sown trees spring up in odd places.

In winter the walnut is fairly easily known by its very stout twigs, which bear squat, oval, velvet-surfaced buds at alternate intervals. If in doubt, cut a twig on the slant and note the much-divided pith at its heart. Walnut bark is grey and resembles that of an ash tree, since it is smooth at first and furrowed later. The compound leaf, too, is like that of ash, but a second glance brings out clear points of difference. Walnut leaves are set alternately, never in opposite pairs; their leaflets are fewer, normally seven, and each is broader and more rounded. Finally, if you crush a walnut leaf you will at once note a rich aromatic odour never found in ash. The juice of the leaves will stain your fingers brown; it was once used as a "sun tan lotion" by gypsies who wished to look even darker.

Walnut comes into leaf late, about mid-May, and at the same time the male and female catkins open, both on the same twigs. The female catkins are groups of two or three flowers set near branch tips. The drawing on page 61 shows a female flower. Male catkins droop downwards, like greenish caterpillars. They are built up of numerous flowers around a central stalk, and each flower has a basal bract, two smaller bracteoles, and about four green sepals; within these are set from ten to twenty stamens that scatter golden pollen on the wind.

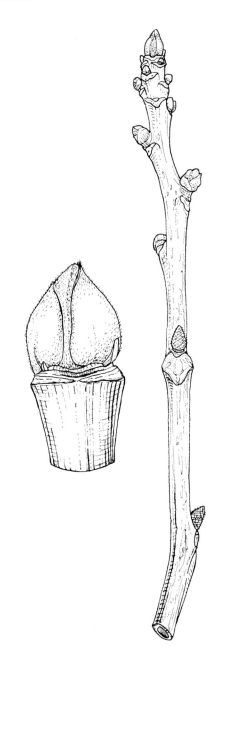

PLATE LXIII
Winter twig, showing male catkin buds below, female catkin buds higher up, and leaf and shoot buds at its tip (life size). Left, a shoot bud ($\times$ 5).

PLATE LXIV
Germinating walnut; the seed-leaves remain within the shell ($\times \frac{1}{2}$).

Walnut flowering in May, with leaves just opening and a male catkin near base of twig ($\times \frac{2}{3}$). Above, male flower ($\times 6$). Below, female flower ($\times 2$).

Walnuts at the green stage in September, with a leaf and a nut partly split to show brown nutshell and green outer husk (all $\times \frac{2}{3}$)

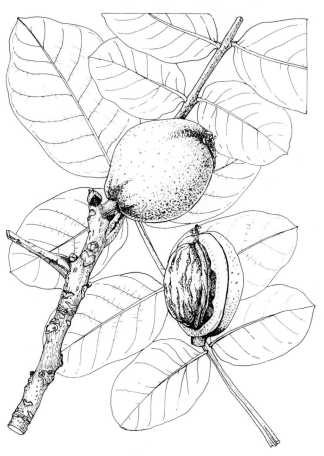

Each female catkin consists of from one to four flowers, shaped like little green flasks. The smooth outer surface of each flower consists of fused bracts, and the tips of four small green sepals can just be seen protruding above it. Beyond this come two large, feathery, purple stigmas. After pollination, these flowers ripen rapidly into fruits, and the drawing on the left shows walnuts at their "green" stage. Each flower produces a single seed, the familiar walnut with its hard wrinkled shell, but this is at first surrounded by a green, fleshy "husk." Walnuts gathered at the "green" stage, before the shell has fully hardened, are used for pickling; later the green husk withers and the brown shell is exposed. Each shell has two sections or "valves," and the embryo plant within it has two

61

wrinkled fleshy seed leaves or cotyledons. These are the delicious walnut kernels which we like to eat raw or in confectionery.

When a walnut is sown, the seed leaves remain within the shell, and the first shoot bears normal leaves, having fewer leaflets than usual.

Most walnuts stand out in the open, where they grow very broadly spreading crowns of lustrous foliage. The timber is a rich greyish brown in colour, but varies greatly as it often includes patches of darker brown, black, or paler brown that give it a lively and attractive figure. It is widely used for high-class furniture, in wood-carving, for the turning of wooden bowls and platters, and as wooden table-ware generally. Because of its high cost much is used as veneer over less expensive timbers. Really big butts, suitable for the cutting of decorative veneers that can be made up into matched patterns, fetch very high prices indeed, and for this reason large old walnut trees have become scarce. Walnut wood is naturally durable, mechanically strong, and very stable; these qualities make it the best of all timbers for gun-stocks.

PLATE LXVII
A magnificent open-grown walnut tree.

62

Platanus acerifolia

Plane

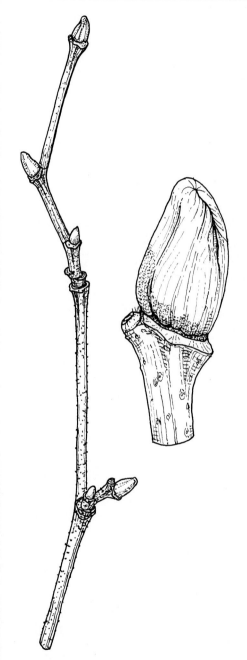

PLATE LXVIII
Winter twig of plane, showing angular trend and ribbing below the alternately-set buds (life size). Right, a single bud showing the conical shape and the scar of last-year's leaf-stalk base, which almost encircles the bud's base ($\times$ 5).

The common plane tree, which is also called the London plane because it is so widely planted in the London streets and squares, has a curious ancestry. No planes are native to Britain, but early in the seventeenth century gardeners introduced the Oriental plane, *Platanus orientalis*, from Asia Minor, and about the same time the American plane, *P. occidentalis*, was brought in from the eastern states of North America. Neither of these trees is fully hardy in Britain; they are only occasionally seen in gardens, and seldom set seed. About 1675, botanists noticed a new race of planes of exceptional vigour and hardiness, which had apparently arisen through chance cross-breeding between the two sorts. Nobody can now say where this happened, probably in southern France or in Spain. London plane is usually increased by cuttings, as it rarely sets fertile seed. Seedlings may resemble one or the other of their original parent trees, or show intermediate characters.

The plane is easily recognised in winter by the unique shape of its buds. They are set alternately on the twigs and are *conical* in outline, rather like a dunce's cap; only one outer scale can be seen, and there is a scar at its base that almost completely encircles the bud. This scar marks the point of detachment of a leaf-stalk. The plane's leaf-stalk has a *swollen* base which conceals the young bud that is growing beneath it—a rare feature that aids recognition.

Plane leaves are distinctly stalked and broadly lobed with from 3 to 7 lobes; they have a close resemblance to those of the sycamore (*Acer pseudoplatanus*, see page 15). In America, the name "sycamore" is often applied to the native planes, whilst in Scotland the name "plane" is frequently used for sycamore, that is *Acer*, trees! But the *alternate* arrangement of leaves and buds marks out the London plane distinctly. A main vein runs out to each lobe, and ends in a pointed tip. The leaves are light-green in colour and fade to a rich brown in autumn; they are leathery in texture and persist on the ground long through the winter.

Young twigs and branches have an olive-grey bark, but as the trunk and main stems mature they shed their outer bark in large flakes and reveal pale creamy-yellow patches of fresh bark below. This results in an unusual, easily recognised and gaily dappled tree trunk, for the process is repeated in different places throughout the life of the tree.

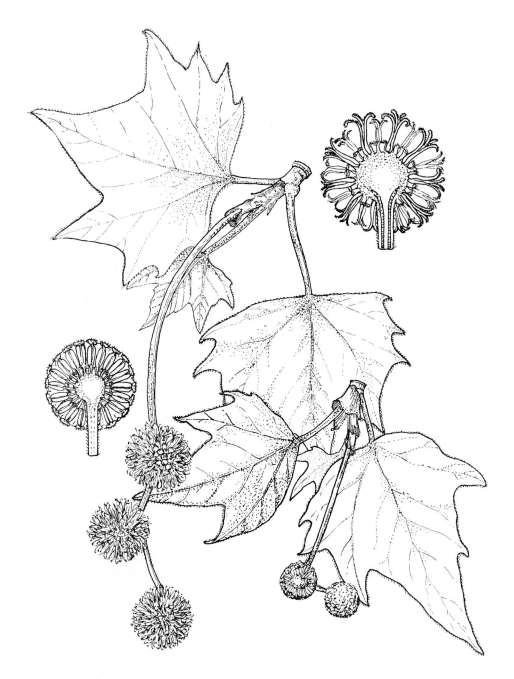

PLATE LXIX
Leaves and flowers of plane in May (life size), with sections of
male and female inflorescences (× 2). Each leaf has three to seven
irregular lobes. Male flowers (left) grow in series of bundles or
"bobbles"; each has three to four sepals, petals and stamens.
Female flowers (right) grow in an outwardly similar series of
bundles on a separate stalk; each has three to four sepals, petals,
and carpels.

PLATE LXX
Plane seedling a few weeks after germination. The two seed-leaves
are narrow and sickle-shaped, and the first true leaf is a simple
one, scarcely lobed at all (× ½).

64

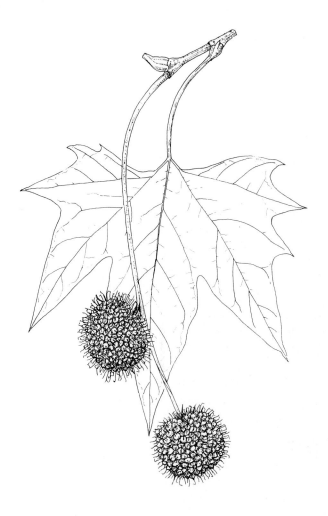

PLATE LXXI
Leaf, winter bud, and fruit clusters of plane in autumn ($\times \frac{2}{3}$).
Each flower has become a tiny rounded fruit that will shortly
release a single seed, tipped with bristly hairs. The projecting
points are the old flower-styles.

In this way the plane rids itself of old bark in which the
vital breathing pores, or lenticels, are becoming clogged
with soot. Even the trunks of trees must breathe-in oxygen,
and the bark-shedding habit helps the tree to survive in
smoky towns, though late leafing and early leaf-fall are more
significant.

Planes bear male and female flowers on the same tree, but in
separate clusters, or inflorescences. They open in May and
the two sexes look much alike. Each inflorescence is a round
ball or "bobble" set on a long hanging stalk; there may be
one, two or three bobbles placed at intervals along the
same stalk. The male inflorescence is a globular structure of
small flowers, each no more than a cluster of three to four
minute green sepals, and a like number of minute green
petals and well-developed stamens; the anthers scatter
pollen on the wind and then the whole male flower group
falls away.

The female bobbles hold scores of very simple flowers,
each having a cluster of three to four bract-like sepals and
petals at the base, topped by four carpels having single
styles and stigmas. After pollination, the whole bobble
changes from green to brown; it is ripe by autumn and
during the winter it gradually breaks up. Each little fruit
falls away from the central stalk and is carried away by the
wind. It consists of four nut-like seeds, each carrying a
tuft of fine yellow hairs. The drifts of plane seed look untidy
and some people find the hairs irritating, but these are the
plane's only faults.

Most seed proves infertile, but where seedlings do arise
they are easily identified. Each has a pair of sickle shaped
seed-leaves, arched back from the central stalk; the early
true leaves are simple in outline; lobed leaves appear later.

The timber of plane has a general resemblance to beech,
being fawn in colour, hard, strong, and easily worked in
any direction. It is not naturally durable out of doors. The
small amount available is usually applied to indoor uses,
such as high-class furniture or wood carving. Large logs
are cut into veneers, by methods that expose the lively
figure of the pith rays, and because of the intricate pattern
then revealed, these veneers are sold as "lacewood."

Plane has proved the most satisfactory of all trees for
street planting in London and other large cities of southern
England, and also in France, Spain, Italy and neighbouring
lands. It grows vigorously under difficult conditions of
polluted air and restricted root space, and is easily held to a
limited size, where that is necessary, by repeated prunings.
It forms a beautiful, well-balanced crown, which casts
welcome shade on hot sunny days without itself appearing
dark or gloomy, while its bark is a cheerful feature even in
the winter months. Many trees in the London squares are
now 200 years old, and have reached heights of 100 feet
with girths of ten feet. Records are 132 feet tall for a magnificent tree beside the ponds at Carshalton, Surrey, and
26 feet round for a tree in the Bishop's Palace grounds at
Ely, Cambridgeshire, reputedly planted about 1674!

PLATE LXXII
A fine open-grown London plane in Kew Gardens, Surrey. Note
the dappled bark.

Populus alba   White Poplar

The poplar trees, of the genus *Populus*, comprise a very large number of species, native to Europe, Asia, and North America, and an even larger number of hybrids between them. Many of these are represented in the unique populetum, or collection of living poplars, maintained at the Forestry Commission's Research Station at Alice Holt, south-west of Farnham in Surrey.

Though no single simple feature marks out the *Populus* genus, poplars are in practice easily known by a group of characters. Their twigs are ribbed or angular in outline, their buds many-scaled and alternately set, their leaves show a random pattern of veins (see page 85), and their branches are likewise random and irregular (see page 74). Poplar leaves are nearly always simple in outline, but the White and Grey poplars bear lobed leaves on their less vigorous twigs. Poplar leaves are always long-stalked, and the leaf-stalk, or petiole, is flattened from side to side (see page 85). This leads to a perpetual fluttering motion, which is very marked in the aspen (see page 5).

Most poplars are easily increased by cuttings, and this feature enables timber growers and gardeners to propagate new kinds rapidly, cheaply, and certainly. Strains of trees or plants that are increased by vegetative means in this way are called "clones" or "cultivars", and their names are printed in Roman type with a capital letter and *single* quotation marks, e.g. *Populus* 'Regenerata.' A few kinds, such as the aspen, will not grow readily from cuttings and must be increased by seed or sucker shoots. Suckers are shoots that arise naturally from underground roots; they are common and indeed troublesome with some poplars, though absent from most.

During the brief flowering season in March, before the leaves open, the poplar genus is easily known by its remarkable catkins. Male and female catkins always appear on separate trees. Male catkins (see page 71) are long slender structures that look dark red at first, but are later tinged with golden pollen. Each catkin carries about fifty separate flowers, and each flower consists of a basal bract and a green cup holding numerous stamens. Pollination is by wind and the male catkins fall in April.

Female catkins (p. 71) are looser, more open structures, that have been likened to necklaces or strings of beads. Each carries about fifty flowers, and every flower consists of a single green bract, a basal cup, and a pear-shaped green ovary tipped by four styles. These flowers ripen rapidly to small green fruit-pods (see page 77), and about midsummer the pods split to release masses of tiny seeds. Each seed bears a tuft of fine white hairs. These hairs carry the seed on the winds, but are considered a nuisance by gardeners, since the mass of fluff makes paths and lawns untidy, while they also stick to fresh paint! For this reason, most nurserymen prefer to sell male poplars, raised as cuttings from *male* trees, because these never shed seed.

Poplar seed has a very short life and cannot be stored or sold commercially. It must be sown within a few days of ripening, and on a moist seedbed. In the wilds, therefore, poplars only spring up in marshy places, or along streamsides, where bare, damp soil or mud is available for colonisation in midsummer. Seedlings have two blunt seed-leaves, followed by normal foliage, and grow rapidly.

Poplar wood has remarkable, distinct characters that ensure peculiar uses. It is pale cream to white in colour, and has large water-conducting vessels. When freshly felled and full of sap it is very heavy, but after it has been seasoned, and the vessels only hold air, it is remarkably light. These features make it worthless for most constructional jobs, but it has another character, a supple toughness and resistance to splitting or splintering, that makes it the best of all timbers for matches, match-boxes, and chip baskets for holding fruit or vegetables. The matches, matchboxes, and basket slats are all cut from *veneers*. Veneers are thin sheets of wood cut from a round log by turning it, on a special lathe, against a long sharp knife. Knots would cause holes in the veneer and poplars are therefore grown in a special way, so as to avoid this fault.

Commercial strains of poplar are increased by striking cuttings, using branches from a named rootstock. After each cutting has taken root it is lifted, the thin first branches are cut back, and it is replanted as a "stumped cutting." One good bud is always left and this forms a straight, upright, fast-growing *set*. The set is planted out on fertile, well-watered land of agricultural quality, trees being spaced at least twenty feet apart. So treated, poplars grow rapidly and are often six feet round and fit for felling after only thirty years. Their lower side branches are pruned off at an early stage, and all the wood formed on the outside of

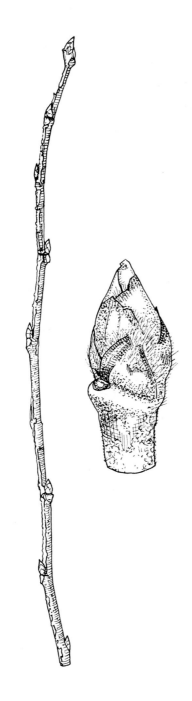

the central core is then *clear*, and will yield knot-free veneer. A few small knots or "buried branches" remain in the centre, but that cannot, in any event, be cut into veneer sheets.

Poplar wood was once used for the bottoms of carts and wheelbarrows because it is light and does not split when stones are thrown on it. Poplar wood fetches the best prices for match-making veneer, but can also serve the same purposes as a softwood—for example in joinery and packing-case making. It is not durable out of doors, unless treated with a preservative. Occasional uses include wood-wool and paper pulp. As a firewood, it is almost useless, for even when seasoned it will only smoulder.

Poplars occasionally cause damage to buildings because their great crowns of foliage, aided by their open large-pored wood, remove water rapidly from the soil during hot, dry summer days. Serious harm only occurs on clay soils in regions of low rainfall—notably London and Essex. There the rapid drying and shrinkage of the clay may be given a directional trend that upsets the foundations of walls and houses. In such places, poplars should never be planted within sixty feet of any structure.

Exact recognition of all the many kinds of poplars is very difficult, even for the specialist, but a few wild and cultivated strains that are not too hard to spot are shown and described here.

White poplar, *Populus alba*, is best known by the white downy undersides of its leaves, the white down that clothes winter twigs and buds, and the creamy white bark on its larger branches and trunks (see page 69). On the shorter, less vigorous twigs its leaves are five-lobed, but on vigorous shoots, even on the same tree, you will find partially-lobed leaves (see page 85) or simple ones having a wavy edge.

An introduced tree, White poplar is naturalized only in the south-east of England, though often grown elsewhere. It often produces sucker shoots, and may form thickets on coastal cliffs, where it resists salt winds. On a clay cliff, it helps to bind soil and so check erosion. Otherwise it is only planted for ornament, as a very effective pale-barked, white-foliaged tree.

PLATE LXXIII
Winter twig and bud of White poplar. Typical poplar features are the angular twigs, with many-scaled buds, set alternately. White poplar bears characteristic white down along twigs and on bud-scales (Twig, life size; bud × 10).

PLATE LXXIV
Female catkins and single flower of White poplar. Male and female catkins appear before leaves on separate trees. Slender female catkins consist of many flowers, each having one green bract, a basal cup and a pear-shaped ovary topped by four styles. (Catkins, life size; flower × 12).

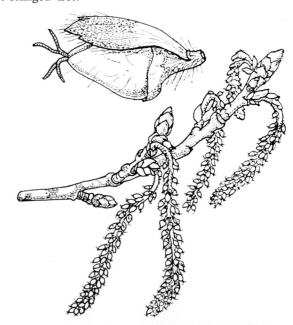

PLATE LXXV
A fine avenue of white poplars, showing the pale bark, smooth
above, rugged at the base.

Populus canescens　　　　　　　　　　　Grey Poplar

Grey poplar is thought to be a natural hybrid between the White poplar (see page 67) and the aspen (see page 82) but by well-established usage it carries a specific name. It can be found growing wild over most of southern England and Wales, and it is occasionally planted for its timber. Its vigour and hardihood, together with the soundness of its timber and freedom from disease, enable it to qualify for Forestry Commission planting grants (see page 77).

The characters of Grey poplar lie midway between those of White poplar and aspen. Its leaves are greyish rather than white underneath, and their shape, though variable, comes closer to the circular aspen leaf than to the lobed leaf of White poplar (see page 85). The bark is heavily ridged and black at the base, with large white, silvery or cream, stippled patches higher up. Suckers arise readily from roots and aid the spread of the tree.

Female Grey poplars are rare in Britain, though they are frequent on the Continent of Europe. In cultivation Grey poplar is usually increased by suckers. Some very large specimens have been recorded; one at Castle Hedingham in Essex measured seventeen feet round while another, at Saling Grove, also in Essex, grew 110 feet tall. They have the same resistance to salt winds as the White poplar, and grow more rapidly on the coastline.

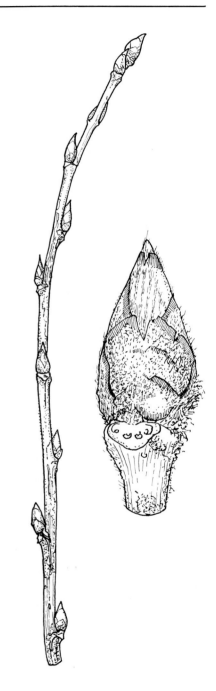

PLATE LXXVI
Winter twig (life size) and bud ($\times$ 7) of the Grey poplar. Both twigs and bud scales are slightly hairy.

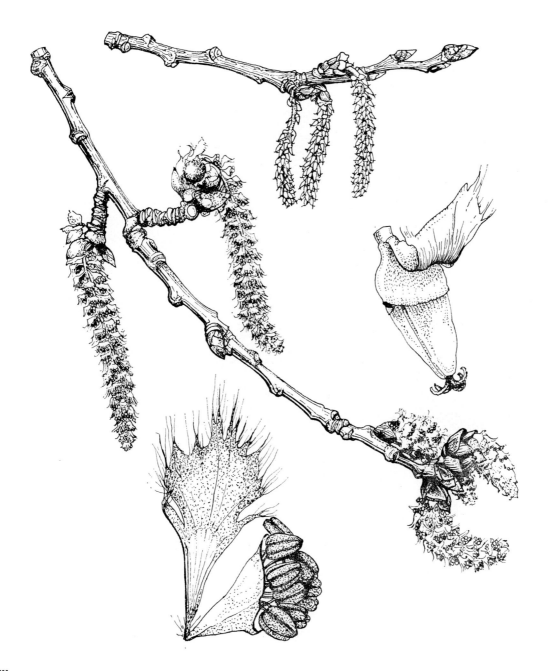

PLATE LXXVII

Male and female catkins of Grey poplar are borne on separate
trees. Male flowers, left, consist of a leafy bract fringed with
hairs, and a green cup holding many stamens. Each female
flower, top right, has a similar bract and cup, with a flask-shaped,
four-styled ovary. (Twigs and catkins, life size; single flowers,
× 12).

PLATE LXXVIII
Grey poplar can form a magnificent specimen tree. The pale
undersides of its foliage are revealed when the wind sweeps
its crown.

Populus nigra

Black Poplar

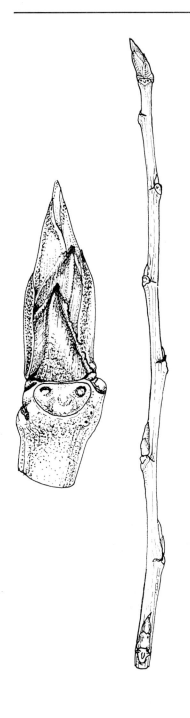

Black poplar, one of our few native kinds, is an uncommon tree. It has been supplanted for commercial planting by the hybrid cultivars that are described on the following pages. Since poplars are not long-lived trees it is tending to vanish from the country scene. Black poplar seldom produces sucker shoots; wild trees are only renewed by seed.

This tree is called "Black" only by way of contrast to the White and Grey kinds. It bark is pale brown and more rugged than that of other poplars. As our photo shows, it forms an upright well-balanced tree having rather random branches retained low down, and a bole that carries typical swellings, which often bear short side shoots. Its leaves (see page 74) are diamond-shaped to oval and, on average, smaller than those of the more popular hybrids. The flowers are typical of the genus, but the female catkins tend to be short and stubby (see page 76).

Black poplar is a hardy and reliable tree, but since it lacks the remarkable hybrid vigour of the cultivars it holds no attractions for the timber grower. You are most likely to find the odd tree growing wild, or cultivated in a park or botanic garden, in the eastern counties of England, though its natural range extends right across the Midlands to the Cheshire plain. Large trees are rare, those recorded as "Black poplars" usually proving to be hybrids.

PLATE LXXIX
Winter twig (life size) and bud ($\times$ 5) of Black poplar, *Populus nigra*. Both are remarkably angular.

PLATE LXXX
Black poplar in an Essex park, showing characteristic swellings
on the bole, erect habit of trunk, and random branches, retained
low down.

Populus nigra variety italica   Lombardy Poplar

Lombardy poplar is a particularly distinctive tree, of great value in landscape planting. Everyone knows its remarkable narrow shape, soaring like a slender plume straight up from a narrow base. Each individual twig follows the upward trend of the main trunk so there are no large branches and the tree never forms a true crown. This habit of growth is called "fastigiate," and it is found as an occasional freak in many sorts of tree. Fastigiate trees are usually hard to propagate, needing careful grafting, but Lombardy poplar can be increased easily by striking cuttings in the soil.

This attractive poplar probably arose in northern Italy, and it draws its name from Lombardy, the great flat plain beside the River Po; it should not be confused with the Black Italian poplar described on page 79. Lombardy poplar was brought to Britain from Turin by Lord Rochford, in 1758. Because the numerous side shoots cause frequent knots and irregularities in the trunk, it has no value as timber and is grown only for ornament or as a shelter or screen tree. A female strain is known, but practically every Lombardy poplar you see is of the male sex. Despite its slender form and appearance of great height, Lombardy poplar is not one of the tallest trees; the current record is 118 feet at Marble Hill, Twickenham, Middlesex.

Lombardy poplar grows rapidly in youth and stands up well to all sorts of adverse conditions, such as town smoke, poor soil, and restricted root room. It is therefore often planted for making, rapidly, a narrow screen to check the wind or to shut out unwanted noise, dust, or an unpleasing view. But it is not an ideal tree for such purposes, since it is not long lived, while the loss or breakage of a single tree seriously disrupts the pattern.

The botanical details of the Lombardy poplar resemble those of the common Black poplar. Growing trees are shown in typical waterside surroundings in Plate I, the crowns in these examples are a little broader than normal; strains differ a little in branching habit.

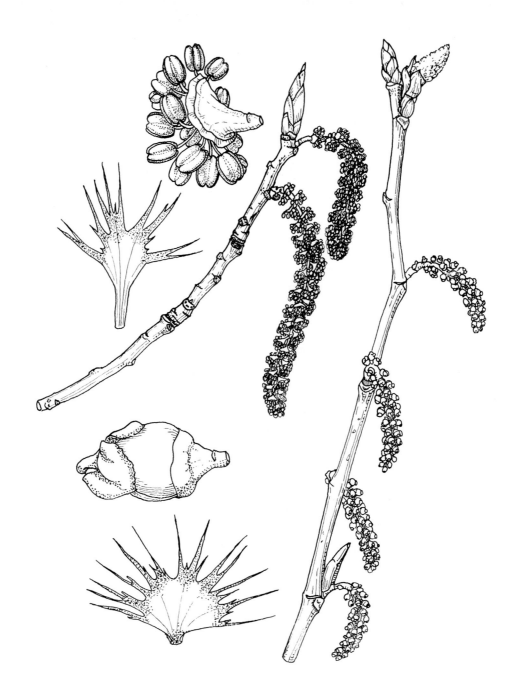

PLATE LXXXI

Top left: Male catkins of the Black Italian poplar, *Populus*
'Serotina', opening in April (life size), with details of a bract
scale and a single male flower ($\times$ 10). The numerous stamens
are borne on a green cup, and the bract scale falls away before
they are ripe. Bottom and right: Female catkins of Black
poplar, *Populus nigra* (life size) with a single female flower and
bract scale ($\times$ 10.) The flower consists of a four-styled carpel
carried on a green cup; the bract scale soon falls off.

Populus 'Regenerata'   A Hybrid Black Poplar

Populus 'Regenerata' is one of the very large number of hybrid strains or cultivars that have arisen through the deliberate or chance cross-breeding of different species. It is believed to have arisen about 1814 through the crossing of the European Black Poplar, *P. nigra* (see page 73) with another hybrid, *P.* 'Serotina' (see page 79).

It is distinguished from that cultivar by: fine willow-like shoots; a shapeless lower crown of *outward* arching branches, retained after they wither; the early flushing of green (not brown) opening leaves; and in being always female (never male).

As *Populus* 'Regenerata' is always a female tree, it has been chosen to illustrate typical seed pods, just opening in June. It is a very vigorous tree and was once widely planted for timber. Unfortunately it has proved susceptible to a serious disease, the Bacterial Canker of Poplar, caused by the bacterium *Pseudomonas syringae*, so its planting can no longer be recommended.

In circumstances like these, foresters naturally turn to a resistant cultivar that will grow equally fast without suffering from the disease concerned. When poplars are planted on a commercial scale for timber, it is most important that effort and money shall not be misdirected into some variety that cannot be expected to grow satisfactorily to full timber size. A good deal of poplar planting is nowadays carried out on fertile land, particularly in the Midlands and South of England, and where the ground is suitable the Forestry Commission makes grants to meet part of the cost. The current figure (in 1970) is £23.17½ per acre planted.

The approved varieties of poplar which are now (in 1970) eligible for planting grants are:

Populus canescens
Populus 'Casale 78' (in Southern England only)
Populus 'Eugenei'
Populus 'Gelrica'
Populus 'Heidemij'
Populus 'Laevigata'
Populus 'Marilandica'
Populus 'Robusta'
Populus 'Serotina'
Populus tacamahaca x *trichocarpa* 32
Populus 'Berolinensis'

Planting sets of these cultivars are raised on a large scale by nurserymen, usually from foundation stocks that have been provided, after appropriate tests for resistance to disease, by the Forestry Commission.

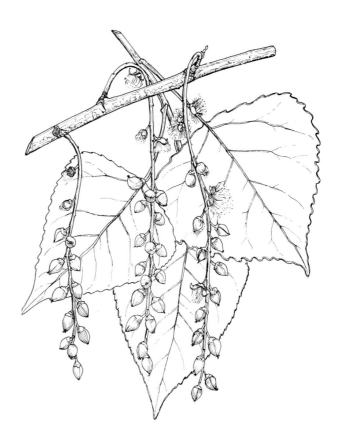

PLATE LXXXII
Leaves and seed pods of a hybrid Black poplar, *Populus* 'Regenerata', which is always a female tree. The leaves are a typical poplar shape—triangular—ovate, and show characteristic random veining. The fruiting catkin is typically necklace-like, and the older seed-pods, near the base of the stalk, are opening to release the hairy-tufted seeds.

PLATE LXXXIII
Hybrid Black poplars grown for timber and shelter on the
Ryston Hall Estate in Norfolk.

Populus 'Serotina'

Black Italian Poplar

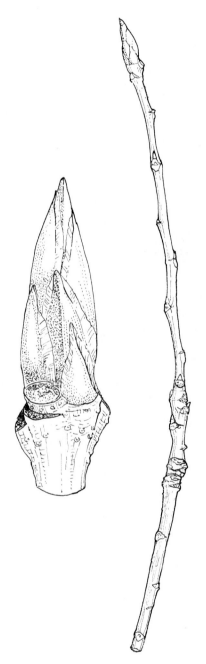

This oddly-named tree is the oldest and best-known of the many hybrid cultivars. Its name of 'Serotina' means "late-leafing," and it is in fact the last of all our poplars to break bud. The early leaves are a warm olive-brown in colour, and form a unique element in the late April scene.

They turn to mid-green as they expand, and their shape is shown on page 85. See page 77 for other points of difference from *Populus* 'Regenerata'.

This tree is called "Black Italian" because it is believed to have originated in Italy, about 1755, by the crossing of the European Black poplar, *P. nigra*, with an eastern American Black poplar, *P. deltoides*. It is now widely planted both in Europe and America.

The Black Italian poplar is always a male tree, and therefore only male catkins can be illustrated here. It has a charac-

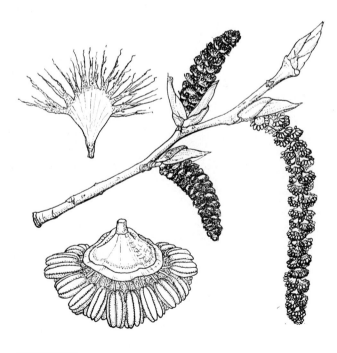

PLATE LXXXV
Male catkins of the Black Italian poplar, opening in April, before the leaves expand (life size). Above left, the bract that opens at the base of each flower, then falls away. Below left, a single male flower, consisting of a green cup carrying numerous stamens. (Both details × 7).

PLATE LXXXIV
Winter twig and bud of the Black Italian poplar. The twig is typically angular, while the bud has several pointed scales. (Twig, life size; bud × 5).

PLATE LXXXVI
Black Italian poplar tree, showing typical irregular branching.

teristic one-sided crown, and looks rather like a huge branch stuck in the ground, rather than a well-balanced tree, (See photo, above). It is hardy, resistant to town smoke, and also resistant to bacterial canker. Individual trees can reach great size, holding over 1,000 cubic feet of timber by the forester's traditional Hoppus measure: this is equivalent to 36 true cubic metres, or a weight of over 36 metric tonnes for the main trunk alone!

Black Italian poplar is often seen as a specimen tree in public parks, particularly in industrial towns. It is still widely planted as a timber producer. The tallest specimen, at Fairlawne, Kent, reaches 140 feet, with a girth of 21 feet.

Populus tacamahaca   Western Balsam Poplar

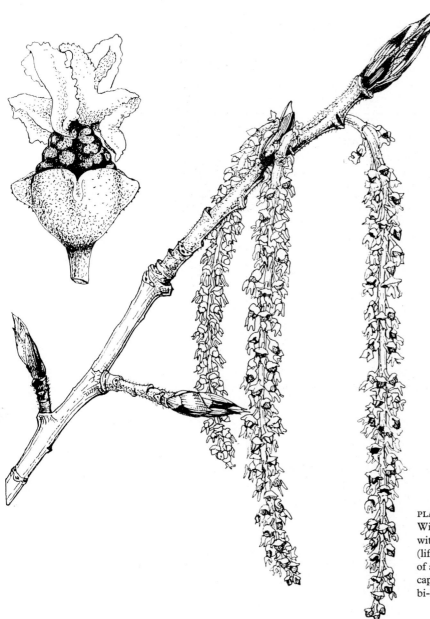

PLATE LXXXVII
Winter twigs and buds of Western Balsam poplar,
with long feathery female catkins opening in April
(life size). The single female flower ($\times$ 9) consists
of a lobed green cup carrying a two-valved
capsule which is topped by two curiously
bi-lobed stigmas. (Basal bract is not shown).

The Balsam poplars, which come from North America and Asia, draw their name from the sweet-smelling sticky gum or balsam that covers their bud scales. This becomes noticeable in spring, just as the leaves open, and often the fragrance fills the air and can be detected many yards away from the trees. The species illustrated here comes from Alaska and northern British Columbia on the western seaboard of North America; there it is also called the Alaskan cottonwood, because of the downy white hairs on its seeds, which in the mass resemble cotton-wool. The specific name, *tacamahaca*, is drawn from a Red Indian name for the poplar tree.

Most balsam poplars are grown as ornamental trees, but there is a hybrid race that is recommended for timber production, particularly in the west of Britain, and qualifies for a planting grant (see page 77). This is *Populus tacamahaca* x *trichocarpa* "32" and it was raised by crossing the Alaskan species with another Balsam poplar that grows farther south in British Columbia, Washington and Oregon.

The drawing shows the remarkably long female catkins, dark carpels and curiously lobed stigmas, that are typical of the Balsam group. The sticky, fragrant winter buds are dark in colour—blue-black rather than brown.

Populus tremula

Aspen

Several features mark out this native poplar from all other kinds. Its leaves are oval or almost round, with a curiously wavy edge (see below and p. 85). They have very slender long stalks that are flattened sideways, and this allows them to tremble or quiver in the slightest breeze. The winter twigs are only slightly angular and the buds have a plump oval outline. Both male and female catkins look remarkably hairy—rather like hairy caterpillars—by reason of their very deeply divided hair-tufted bracts. These are purplish

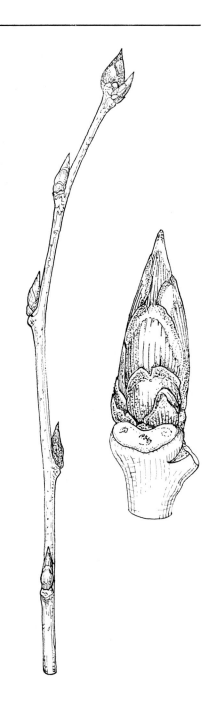

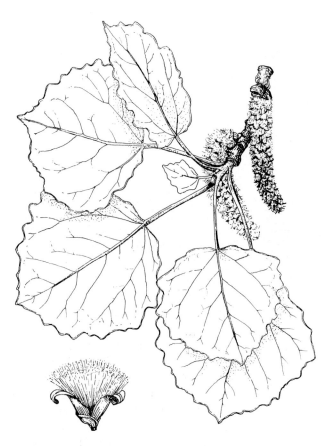

PLATE LXXXVIII
Leaves and fruiting catkins of aspen in May (life size). The single seed-pod, left, is splitting to release the small seeds, each tufted with hairs ($\times$ 7).

PLATE LXXXIX
Winter twig of aspen (life size) with a single stoutly oval bud ($\times$ 5).

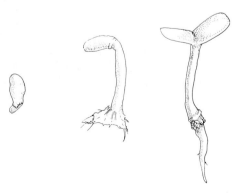

PLATE XC
Aspen catkins in late February. Above: female catkins (life
size) with a single flower (× 12), showing a dark purple hairy
bract, green cup, and conical ovary topped by two bi-lobed stigmas.
Below, male catkins (life size) and a single flower (× 12).
The dark purple, hairy bracts enlarge as the male catkins age.
The stamens are dark purple when young, but appear yellow
with pollen later.

PLATE XCI
The germination of an aspen seed on damp earth in May. Left,
swelling 18 hours after sowing; centre, forming a root and a
shoot 3 days after sowing; right, extending root and opening
two seed leaves, only 6 days after sowing. (× 10).

PLATE XCII
Young aspen trees.

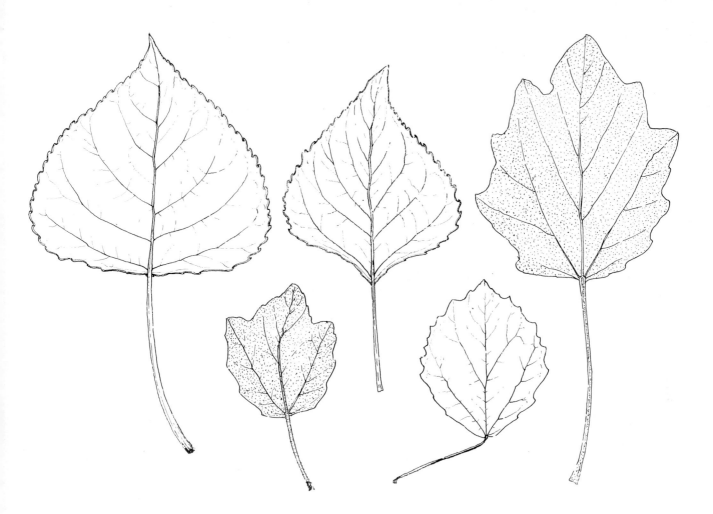

PLATE XCIII
Poplar leaves and leaf-stalks; note random veining of leaves.
All two-thirds natural size. Top left: Black Italian poplar,
Populus 'Serotina' triangular-ovate. Top centre: Native
Black poplar, *P. nigra*, a diamond. Top right: Grey poplar, *P. canescens*, a slightly lobed leaf—shape is variable. Bottom left:
White poplar, *P. alba*, distinctly lobed leaf—shape is variable.
Bottom right: Aspen, *P. tremula*, round, with typically narrow
leaf-stalk, associated with fluttering foliage.

in colour—an unusual hue in the late February scene; on the male tree it contrasts with the plentiful yellow pollen shed by the stamens. The fruiting catkins, which ripen in May, also look very fuzzy, due in this case to numerous white hairs on each little seed.

Cuttings of aspen are hard to strike, so this tree is raised from either sucker shoots detached from the parent tree, or else by seed. The germination of the minute seed, which is only viable for a few days after ripening, is shown on page 83; it is remarkably quick, taking only six days.

Aspen seldom forms a tall tree; it is most often seen as a thicket of sucker shoots in some marshy spot on a clay soil.

Its natural range includes the whole of the British Isles and it is a very hardy tree. Its wood is the best of all timber for match-making, and it is so used in Scandinavia, Poland and Russia. But in Britain it never reaches an acceptable size, so it is never planted for timber here.

The name of "aspen" comes from an old Teutonic word for a poplar tree, represented by *Espe* in German and *osp* in Norwegian. In Gaelic it is called *eubh* or more poetically *cran critheanach*, "the shaking tree" because of the incessant motion of its leaves. The Welsh name is *aethnen*, but it is also called, again because its leaves are never still, *coed tafod merched* or "the tree of the woman's tongue."

85

Prunus avium Wild Cherry

This lovely tree is unique in combining a glorious display of blossom with high value as useful timber. It is native as far north as the Scottish border, but only common as a wild tree amid the beechwoods of the south eastern chalk downs. Many landowners have planted it in mixed woodlands on their private estates, more often for the beauty of its flowers than for any cash return from its wood. It is one of several ancestors of our cultivated orchard cherries, the others being smaller cherries found in south-east, Europe.

Wild cherry can often be picked out by its peculiar bark which is purplish brown in colour, and smooth, with a metallic lustre. It carries well defined lenticels or breathing pores, which are seen as raised corky bands in horizontal lines across the trunk. The bark of old trees sometimes peels away in horizontal strips, and if a trunk or branch is wounded a curious gum, clear yellowish-green in colour, oozes out, to cover the broken tissues.

The winter buds are alternately set and oval, with well-defined bud scales, and have a distinct red-brown colour. Cherry leaves are carried on long stalks and are elliptical in outline; they have a serrated edge and taper to a long point. In the autumn they change from mid-green to fiery shades of orange, crimson and purple and at that time a tall cherry stands out from all surrounding trees like a glowing torch.

Cherry flowers are borne in clusters—a feature that distinguishes the cherry group from the nearly-related plums. Each group holds about four flowers, and they always arise on short shoots along established branches, never on the long shoots that extend the crown.

Each separate flower has a long stalk, five green sepals, five white petals, and a host of yellow stamens. The green pistil at the heart of the flower has a single style and a single seed chamber. There are nectaries at the base of the petals to reward the bees that carry pollen from flower to flower. In most years cherry blossom opens in late April, just after the leaves have expanded and are turning from their early reddish brown to their summer green, so providing a harmonious colour contrast. A late cold spring delays the opening of the leaves but not that of the flowers, which then appear, like a glistening snowdrift, over a framework of bare branches.

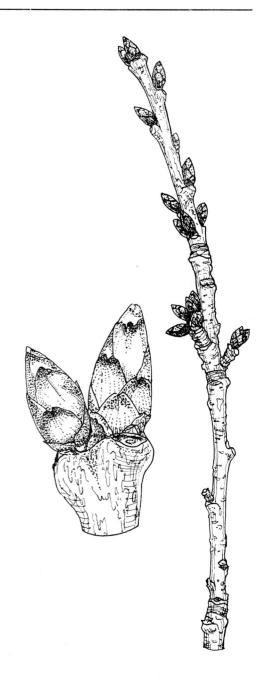

PLATE XCIV
Winter twig of wild cherry (life size); the long shoots at the tip will extend the branch; only the short shoots or "spurs" lower down bear flowers and fruit. Left, buds with well-defined scales ($\times$ 5).

PLATE XCV
Cherry flowers are borne in clusters, each on a single stalk; usually they open in April, just as the leaves expand. Note how they spring from short shoots, with basal bud scales (life size).

PLATE XCVI
Cross section through a single cherry flower, showing reflexed green sepals, white petals, numerous stamens and the central pistil, with a single style above and one ovule within ($\times 1\frac{1}{2}$).

PLATE XCVII
Newly-germinated cherry seedling, with two round, fleshy seed leaves and opposite early leaves; later leaves are set alternately ($\times \frac{1}{2}$).

PLATE XCVIII
Expanded leaves and fruits of wild cherry, ripening in August ($\times \frac{2}{3}$).

PLATE XCIX
The full glory of cherry blossom is best seen in a cold spring
when trees leaf out late, and white flowers smother bare
branches.

Wild cherries ripen quickly, changing from green through red to black between April and June. Each flower produces a single long-stalked fruit, which has a tough black outer skin, a thin layer of sweet yellowish pulp that is quite good to eat, and a large hard black stone—the tree seed—at its centre.

The birds quickly strip the trees and spread the seeds, either by dropping them or swallowing the cherries whole. Seeds that have passed through a bird's gut are believed to germinate in the following spring; otherwise the cherry stone must lie dormant on the forest floor for a whole year before it will sprout. Cherry seedlings have two fleshy round seed leaves that are followed by normal foliage. Planting stocks of wild cherry are always raised from seed, but cultivated kinds are increased by grafting.

Most cherry wood is used for furniture making. Some is employed in fine carving, and the waste branchwood makes a first-rate firewood, which burns with the fragrance of the cherry blossom. Large logs are sliced into decorative veneers. Cherry wood is hard, strong and easy to work. It has a beautiful shade of warm brown, tinged with gold and green, and an intricate, attractive figure.

The wild cherry is also called, particularly in Scotland, the "gean"—pronounced with a hard "g"; this name is derived from an old Italian name, *guina*, for the cultivated cherry tree. It can grow very tall, up to 102 feet, and become quite stout, up to 11 feet round. It is sometimes used as a stock for the many sorts of cultivated cherries, which are always grafted, or for the beautiful ornamental cherries that decorate roadsides and gardens.

Quercus borealis

Red Oak

All the true oaks belong to the genus *Quercus* which is found in temperate zone forests all round the Northern Hemisphere—in Europe, Asia and America. Oaks have certain marked features that make recognition easy. Winter buds are alternately arranged, but towards the tip of the twigs they form distinct *clusters*; as a result of this, oaks branch in an irregular pattern.

The flowers are catkins, which open in May. Male catkins are long-stalked, and carry a succession of small flowers. Each separate male flower has a number of bracts and four to five stamens. After shedding pollen, the male catkins fall away. Female catkins, which are carried on the same tree, are shorter, with fewer flowers. Each individual female flower has several bracts and a three- or four-styled pistil. After pollination, the female flower develops the very distinctive fruit—the acorn. Usually this takes only one season, and the acorns are ripe by October, but some kinds of oaks take two years to ripen their seeds.

Each acorn is a nut or hard, one-seeded fruit. It sits on a peculiar little cup, or cupule, formed by the fusing together of several small leafy bracts to make a hard woody structure. Acorns are spread by animals and birds that eat most of them, but scatter or drop others undamaged. When they sprout in the spring, the seed-leaves remain within the acorn; the first shoot bears a few scale leaves and then normal foliage. Our word "acorn" is compounded of two Anglo-Saxon words—*ac* for oak and *corn* for seed. The seed crop is called "mast," a word related to "meat" in the sense of food, because they make good food for swine.

Heavy crops, or "mast years," are irregular. This aids the spread of the oaks, for in a good mast year more seed falls than the birds and beasts, wild or tame, can readily eat. Other features of the oaks vary widely from one kind to another. These include leaf shape, colour and texture, the character of the bark and the quality of the wood.

Red oak is one of a number of reddish-foliaged kinds that grow wild in North America and have been introduced to Europe as decorative trees. The reddish tints are seldom obvious when the yellowish leaves unfold in spring, and they are masked by a rich green during the summer. But when autumn comes and the leaves fade they blaze out in shades of russet, scarlet or crimson. The leaf shape resembles a flame, being a long irregularly-lobed oval, but it is variable. The acorns are round or dome-shaped and take two years to ripen. The bark is smooth and grey. The slender winter twigs are illustrated on page 104.

The wood of red oak is rather featureless. It is dull brown in colour, reasonably hard and strong, and works well in any direction, but it lacks the remarkable strength, durability and attractive figure of the native English oaks. In America it is used for furniture and small wooden objects, or as firewood. Red oak grows fast, even on soils of moderate fertility, but as there is little demand for its wood it is planted solely for ornament. You may find it in parks or large gardens, or on the fringes of certain national forests where it has been planted to set off the varied greens of the timber trees.

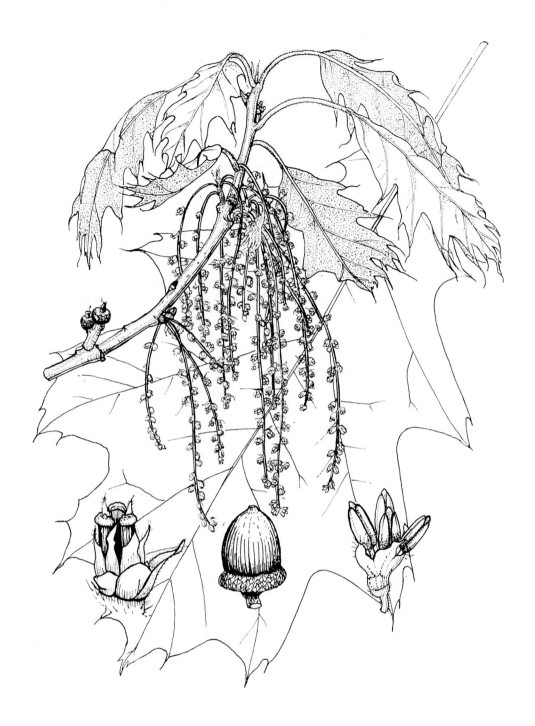

PLATE C
Above: Flowering twig of Red oak, with leaves unfolding in
April, backed by the outline of a mature, flame-shaped, leaf.
A female catkin is seen on the left, male catkins in the centre
(life size). Below, left: Single female flower ($\times$ 15) showing
bracts and three stigmas (sometimes four are found). Below,
centre: Acorn on its cup (life size). Below, right: Single male
flower ($\times$ 10) with bracts and four stamens (sometimes five are
found).

PLATE CI
Red oak tree in spring, with leaves unfolding.

Quercus cerris Turkey Oak

This handsome fast-growing tree is native to Turkey and the adjoining lands of the eastern Mediterranean Zone. It was introduced to Britain about the year 1735 and has now become naturalised. You can often find tall specimen trees in parks, and seedlings on waste ground or woodland fringes. Several distinct features mark it out from our native kind.

The bark is rough, rougher than that of the common oaks,

PLATE CII
Flowering twig of Turkey oak in spring, with male catkins
(life size). Note the long bud stipules. Left, centre: Single male
flower, with bracts and four stamens (× 6). Left, bottom:
Female catkins, made up of two flowers with long hairy bracts
and four styles apiece (× 6).

PLATE CIII
Fruiting twig of Turkey oak ($\times \frac{2}{3}$). Note the remarkably "mossy"
acorn cup.

and deep in its fissures there are streaks of bright tangerine orange colour. The buds are surrounded by very long stipules, as shown in the winter twig picture on page 104. The leaves are longer and narrower than those of common oaks, with a clearer stepped outline to the lobes. Each acorn cup has a covering of soft mossy hairs.

The timber of Turkey oak is highly esteemed in Turkey itself, and is used there for a wide range of fencing and building work, and also for furniture. But as grown under the different climate of Britain it has no attractions to the user and few timber merchants accept it. Tests have shown that it shrinks to a remarkable degree and is apt to warp badly. This is unfortunate since Turkey oak grows faster than the common kinds, forms a straighter trunk, and springs up readily from self-sown acorns. Its only future is as an ornamental tree.

Young trees of Turkey oak retain their brown, faded leaves on their branches right through the winter; they do not fall until the fresh leaves open next spring. Other trees with this singular habit are the common oaks, the beech and the hornbeam; the two last-named trees are often used for hedges that remain leaf-clad right through the winter. This feature is only seen on *low* branches, up to a height of eight feet or so. It is hard to see what advantage, if any, it gives to the trees.

93

PLATE CIV
Turkey oak, in Kew Gardens.

Quercus ilex

Holm Oak

Holm oak is called after the old English name of "holm" for a holly bush, and it is indeed so like a holly that it is often mistaken for one. Its leaves are dark green and leath-ery-textured, with upper glossy surfaces, dark and shiny; the lower surfaces are paler and hairy. These leaves are alternately set and the buds, which are rather small, are

PLATE CV
Above: Leafy spray of Holm oak, bearing male catkins in May; (life size). Below: Leaf and female catkin, also in May (life size). Top left: Single male flower, showing bracts and numerous stamens (× 10). Right: Single female flower, with bract, cupule, and four-styled pistil (× 10).

clustered near the tips of the twigs, in the typical pattern for oaks. The bark is black and rugged, being divided into small squares.

Holm oak bears male and female catkins in May in the characteristic form of all the oaks. Its acorns are unusual in needing nearly two years to ripen; they mature in October. They germinate fairly readily even in Britain, and at one or two places on the south coasts of England and Wales this unusual tree has become naturalised. It is native to the Mediterranean region and its evergreen foliage reflects the peculiar climate found there. The winter is rainy but fairly warm, so evergreen leaves are needed to make good use of an unusual growing season. The summers are dry and hot, so thick, waxy foliage is required to check undue loss of moisture. Each leaf has a life of about four years, and there is a steady fall of spent leaves—overshadowed by those growing further out—each autumn.

Holm oak was brought to Britain in the sixteenth century, but has only been planted as an ornamental tree. It is completely resistant to salt in the air, so it is often chosen for shelterbelts close to the coast. But its sombre evergreen foliage casts a very dense shade, and nothing whatsoever can be grown beneath it. After a hard winter the foliage often looks brown, but it resumes its green colour later. Holm oaks are very wind-firm.

The wood is very strong, hard and dense, but difficult to work. It is curiously patterned with dark brown and light brown and shows "silver grain" along its rays. It is only used for decorative wood-carving, or else as firewood. The largest trees are all in the South of England, where they may reach heights of 80 feet and girth up to 20 feet, with broad spreading crowns, and live to be 250 years old.

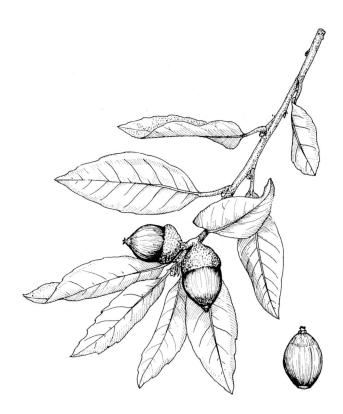

PLATE CVI
Evergreen leaves and ripening acorns of Holm oak in October ($\times \frac{2}{3}$).

PLATE CVII
A grand old Holm oak in Kew Gardens, Surrey.

Quercus petraea   Sessile Oak

Two kinds of oak are native to Britain, but they often hybridize and many intermediate forms occur. The typical Sessile oak is distinguished by the fact that its female flowers, and the resulting acorns, are stalkless, and sit directly on the twigs. Its leaves, however, are distinctly stalked. (See cover and pictures, page 99.)

In contrast, the Pedunculate oak, *Quercus robur*, bears its female flowers and acorns, singly or in groups, on definite stalks or peduncles. Its leaves, as shown on page 99, are stalkless or nearly so.

Another fairly constant point of distinction is the acorn shape. Sessile oak has short acorns, bluntly conical in outline, that taper steadily from base to tip. (See cover.) The acorns of Pedunculate oak become stouter for about two thirds of their length, before they taper sharply to a blunt point, and they are distinctly longer.

Tree form varies greatly, but it is generally held by foresters that the Sessile oak has the better trunk of the two, more likely to persist high into the crown and yield good lengths of timber. Timber merchants, however, find no other differences between the woods of the two sorts of tree, and laboratory tests have confirmed their similarity. Both are marketed as "English oak."

Sessile oak is often said to be more typical of the lighter soils in the north and west of the British Isles, whereas Pedunculate oak takes the lead on the heavier clay soils farther south and east. But owing to the widespread planting of both kinds, in woods in nearly every district, it is no longer possible to find clear-cut zones occupied by each sort. See foot of p. 102 for record sizes.

Sessile oak springs up readily from chance-sown seeds, carried by birds or beasts. Most years are irregular, but at one time acorns were so important to rural economy that woods were measured in terms of the number of swine that their oaks would support. A typical entry in the Domesday Book, compiled on the orders of William the Conqueror about A.D. 1086 says of a certain village: "There is wood for forty swine," and the village was taxed accordingly!

As more and more woods were cleared for farming, oak timber increased in value, for it had exceptional utility in country life. The heartwood of English oak has a warm, rich, deep brown colour and is naturally durable; there is a

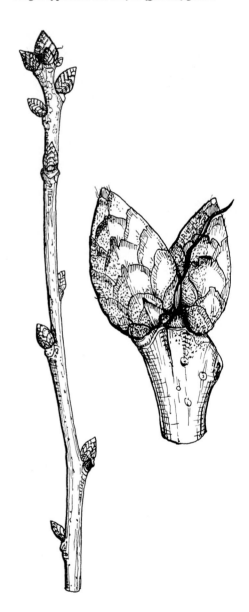

Winter twig of Sessile oak (life size), and two buds ($\times$ 4). The clustering of the buds at the top of the twig is typical of the oak, or *Quercus*, genus.

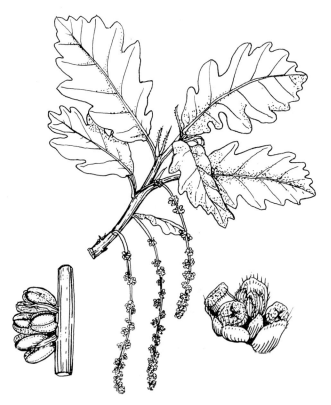

Oak branchwood is a good fuel, and it can also be made into first-rate charcoal. Even the bark is valuable, for it is rich in tannin; before imported bark and wood extracts, or tanning chemicals, were invented, it was the mainstay of the leather tanning industry.

After the virgin forests had been cleared, oaks were cultivated in various ways to meet these needs. Some were grown as coppice, cut over every twenty years or so to yield firewood or charcoal wood, fence posts, or mine props, along with a regular harvest of valuable tanbark. This is no longer profitable, but many coppiced woods remain in western valleys, and are often mistaken for untouched natural woodland. Other oaks were grown to larger sizes, over a lifetime of 100 years or even more, to give big building timber. On many estates, they were spaced wide apart, as "standard" trees amid coppices of hazel or other small shrubs; this arrangement gave short-boled timber, but a large proportion of stout curved branchwood suitable for ship building. Today, however, the only real demand is for stout, straight logs that will yield long, thick planks at the sawmill. To secure these, oaks must be grown more closely together in plantations, and thinned out at intervals to encourage steady growth without undue branching.

PLATE CIX
Flowering twig of Sessile oak (life size). Below, left: Single male flower, consisting of a cluster of bracts and stamens ($\times$ 10). Below, right: Two female flowers, consisting of bracts and four-styled pistils, which arise directly from a twig ($\times$ 10).

paler-coloured band of sapwood around this, which has, little durability, but this is quite thin and could easily be allowed for when the timber was worked up. Oak is strong and so hard that it presents problems in shaping and nailing—ordinary wire nails, for example, cannot be driven into it, but it can readily be secured with screws or pegs. The wide, easily-seen rays that run from the centre of the log to its circumference give it an attractive figure, which may be revealed by skilful cleaving or sawing as "silver grain." These rays also make it easy for a craftsman to cleave logs into segments with axe or wedge, and oak can be readily hewn with an adze to squared outlines.

Before power saws and sawmills were developed, country carpenters shaped building timbers with simple hand tools —axe, saw, wedge, and adze. All the half-timbered buildings that have survived the centuries were wrought in this way, and their timber is nearly always oak. Sailing ships of all kinds, from small fishing vessels to mighty men-of-war like Nelson's famous *Victory*, were built of oak heartwood, shaped by hand into a cunning pattern of ribs, crooks and knees. Oak, especially if cleft, makes an excellent fencing timber; it will serve well for both upright posts and horizontal rails. Other specialised uses are as wheel spokes, ladder rungs, and barrel staves. Much was used, as it still is today, for furniture of all kinds.

PLATE CX
Fruiting twig of Sessile oak with short, conical acorns, tapering steadily towards the tip, sitting directly on the twigs ($\times$ ⅔). Note the distinct leaf stalks.

99

PLATE CXI
A fine Sessile oak in Alice Holt Forest, Hampshire, seen in spring. Its typical erect trunk persists well up amidst the crown of branches.

Quercus robur   Pedunculate Oak

Pedunculate oak is distinguished from the Sessile oak by its female flowers and acorns being set on long stalks, and also by its almost stalkless leaves. It is probably the commoner of our two native oaks, and may in fact be our commonest tree. A Forestry Commission census of trees and woods taken in 1947 showed that, at that date, oaks occupied one third of the woodland area, while every third tree along the hedgerows was also an oak. This shows how well adapted

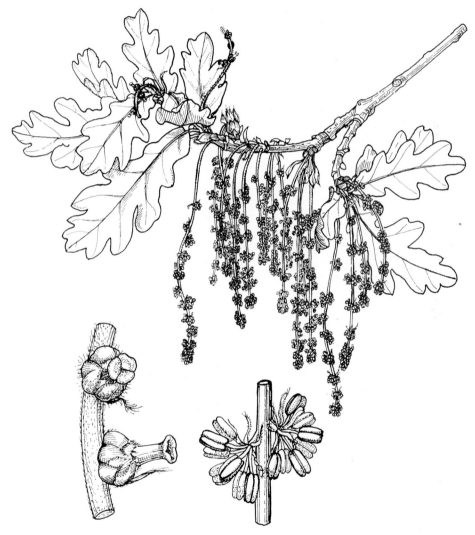

PLATE CXII
Oak seedling (× ½).

PLATE CXIII
Flowering twig of Pedunculate oak (life size) showing two groups of female flowers, on long stalks, at the left, and male catkins in the centre. Below, left: Two female flowers on their long stalk (× 7); each has a cluster of bracts and a three-styled pistil. Below, right: Two male flowers on their catkin stalk; each is a bundle of bracts and stamens.

the oaks are to the British climate and to most of our varied soils, though you will not find them on the poorest land, nor in exposed places amid the hills.

Oakwoods are still being planted today, though only on a modest scale. This is because oak takes so long to mature, and is slow to produce any considerable volume of marketable timber. The smaller sizes of oak timber, such as that from young trees removed from plantations during thinnings, or from mature trees holding much branchwood, fetch low prices. But large, straight stems are always valuable, though they take a hundred years or more to mature. Most of them are sawn into planking which is used for high-class joinery and furniture. Some are cut or sliced along the radius or "true quarter" of the log, to expose the beautiful silver grain, which is used as a surface veneer over ordinary timbers.

Forest oaks begin life as sturdy seedlings in a nursery bed. Their large seed, the acorn, enables them to put down a long tap root and to send up a sturdy shoot in their first season. They may be planted in the woods at that age, or else be transplanted to another nursery bed, where they spend a second year, growing larger and developing a more bushy root system. In the woods they are planted about four feet apart, rather closer than other trees, to encourage early upward growth, and to discourage side branching in their youth. Close spacing also provides a surplus of trees for removal as thinnings, leaving the better ones to remain to form the "final crop" of mature timber. For the first few years an oak plantation looks rather scrubby, for the little trees start growth slowly and need repeated weedings each summer. By degrees a large proportion develop into tall straight poles. As they grow larger the survivors from the thinnings develop large, spreading crowns and start to bear flowers and seed. Eventually, perhaps 120 years after planting, the whole stand is felled for the sawmill, and the land is replanted.

The annual rhythm of life for the oak begins in April, when the buds burst and the soft green leaves, tinged with brownish red, expand. The shoot buds elongate to give the first extension of the tree's branchwood. Later in the season there is a second, further extension that is very characteristic of the oak, though it is also found in beech and many other trees. This is called "Lammas growth" because it is most marked in midsummer, though Lammas Day is actually the first of August. At that time long shoots, carrying rapidly-expanding leaves which are, at first, crimson in colour, grow out and extend the crown.

Open-grown oaks often bear catkins and fruits while quite young, no more than twenty years old, but in the woods flowering is usually delayed until the trees have stood for forty years or so. Catkins open in May, just after the leaves have expanded, and acorns ripen in October. In a mild autumn they start to sprout at once, but those that are needed for sowing by the forester are stored through the winter in cool, moist surroundings, such as a well-ventilated earth pit, protected from the rain and from

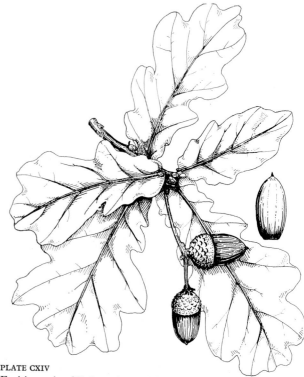

PLATE CXIV
Fruiting twig of Pedunculate oak ($\times \frac{2}{3}$); the acorns are oblong, becoming broader towards the tip, then tapering. The leaves are stalkless.

marauding birds or squirrels.

The oak's active year ends with the fall of the leaves, which fade to bright brown as winter approaches.

Oaks are remarkable in being able to endure a variety of fungal diseases and insect plagues without suffering lasting harm. The most conspicuous types of damage are the galls formed by small gall-wasps that lay eggs in developing tissues. Abnormal growth results, and a tiny grub or larva grows up within the gall, feeding on the oak's substance. Common forms are the Marble gall, which forms in place of a shoot and is hard, brown and round, and the Oak-apple, a soft pinkish-white outgrowth on the leaves; there may also be quaint round Spangle-galls on the leaves, Currant-galls on the male catkins, and yet other galls below ground on the tree's roots. The Oak Leaf-roller moth, *Tortrix viridana*, so called because its grub rolls over a leaf so that it can pupate beneath it, may become so numerous that its voracious caterpillars strip nearly every leaf from a whole wood. But the oaks survive such mishaps with only a small decrease in annual growth.

individual trees can reach great girths, the present record being held by a Sessile oak at Pontfadog, near Chirk in Denbighshire, which is 42 feet 9 inches round. Trees of this thickness are certainly several hundred years old, though it is doubtful if any oak lives to score one thousand summers. Strange to say, oak is not among our tallest trees; the height record, 135 feet, which is held by a Sessile tree at Whitfield in Herefordshire, has often been exceeded by lime and elm.

PLATE CXV
Pedunculate oak in summer, showing characteristic branching
habit. The trunk of an open-grown tree is soon lost amid a
maze of branches.

PLATE CXVI

Winter twigs and buds of three oaks. Twigs two-thirds
natural size; buds magnified three times. Left: Red oak, with
slender twigs and narrow, tapering buds. Centre: Turkey oak,
with clusters of stipules on every bud. Right: Pedunculate
oak, with rugged twigs and stoutly oval buds.

Robinia pseudoacacia

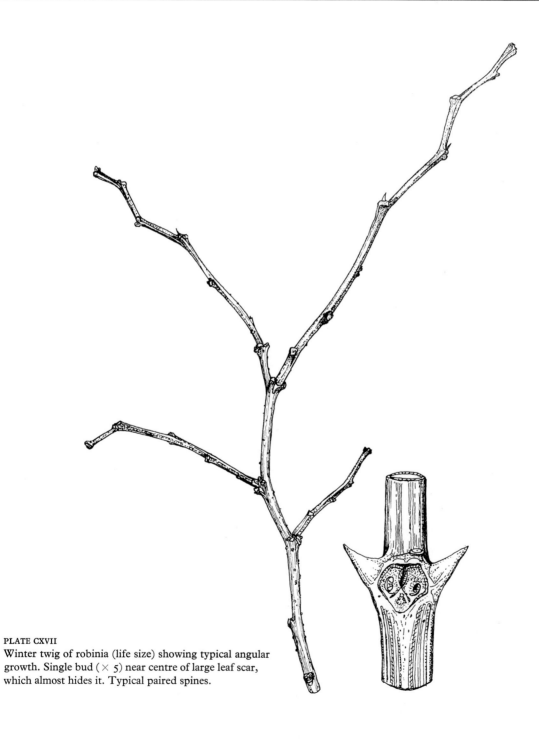

PLATE CXVII
Winter twig of robinia (life size) showing typical angular
growth. Single bud ($\times$ 5) near centre of large leaf scar,
which almost hides it. Typical paired spines.

PLATE CXVIII
Flowering shoot of robinia in June, showing pinnately compound leaves and hanging racemes of white Sweet pea-shaped blossoms (life size). Single flower (× 2) with calyx of sepals, large "standard" petal at top, "wings" at sides, and "keel" below.

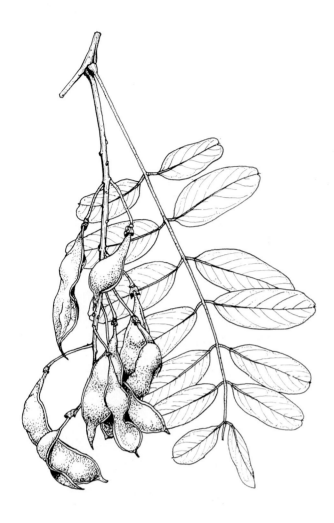

PLATE CXIX
Fruiting twig of robinia ($\times \frac{3}{4}$).

The robinia is named after Jean Robin, a French botanist who first described it in 1601, shortly after it was introduced to Europe from its home in the south-eastern states of North America. It is also called the "locust tree" because early settlers thought it might be the tree that nourished John the Baptist in the wilderness, though its seeds are no good to eat! Yet another name is "acacia" or "false acacia", again from a false identification with a Biblical tree, because it carries little spines, always in pairs, at the base of each leaf.

Robinia is easy to identify, since no other commonly planted tree bears such *paired* spines; the winter buds beside them are virtually invisible, being small, scale-less and hidden by the base of the fallen leaf stalk. The scar of the old leaf stalk is large. The leaves are a little like those of an ash tree, but are alternately set (not opposite) and have more rounded leaflets. The pale grey bark on old stems becomes thick and is patterned with irregular ribs.

Flowers, which are carried in profusion on the crowns of tall trees in June, are white and hang in long drooping racemes. Each separate blossom resembles a Sweet pea flower, for robinia belongs to the same family, the Leguminoseae. It has five green sepals and five white petals set in a typical pattern—a large "standard" at the back, two "wings" at the sides, and two petals at the front folded together to form a "keel." This arrangement helps to guide a visiting bee, in search of nectar, over the five stamens that dust it with yellow pollen, and close to the one-chambered pistil at the centre. Seed pods, which ripen by October, are greyish, hard, swollen and bent, and hold several hard black seeds.

The wood of robinia is golden yellow in colour, with a paler sapwood fringe. It is hard, strong and naturally durable, and the American settlers made great use of it for fencing, tool handles, cart shafts and other exacting purposes. Unfortunately the trunk is nearly always twisted and fluted, and now that sawmills have succeeded hand tools, for working up timber, it is scarcely ever used. Robinia is grown simply as an ornamental tree in parks and large gardens. It is unsuitable for smaller ones since it drops a varied litter of spent blossom, faded leaves and seed pods, and is apt to send up strong sucker shoots from its roots. These roots carry the nodules, typical of the Sweet pea family, which hold bacteria that enable the plant to "fix" the nitrogen of the air; this enables robinia to thrive on poor soils, so it is sometimes used to cover slag heaps.

PLATE CXX
Robinia makes a handsome ornamental tree, but its twisted
and fluted trunk lessens its value as timber

Salix alba   White Willow

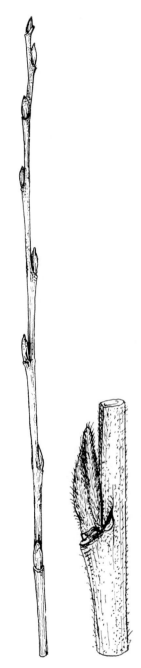

Willows stand out from all other trees through features peculiar to their genus, which is called *Salix* and gives its name to the family Salicaceae. But within this genus there are many species, varieties and hybrids, which baffle the experts, and the willows range in size from tall trees through shrubs to prostrate forms that creep over the surface of the ground. Four common tree forms are described here.

Willow buds have several scales but only *one* bud scale can ever be seen on the outer surface; this is a useful feature for identification, since only the plane with its distinctive conical bud (see page 63) shows this feature too. The buds are always alternately set, but vary considerably in size and shape, as our drawings show.

Willow leaves are always simple in outline, never lobed or compound. Their shape varies, according to species, from broad ovals through ellipses to long, narrow lanceolate outlines.

With rare exceptions in a few ornamental kinds, willow trees are always wholly male or wholly female. In their early stages the familiar "pussy willow" outline of both sexes look much alike, and a close look is needed to say which is which. Later, the stamens, with their golden pollen, become obvious on the male tree. Catkins on female trees remain whitish green in colour, and eventually become downy as their seed pods open to release tiny seeds, each tipped with white hairs. Most willows flower in March, just before their leaves open, but a few delay flowering until May. Wind is the main agent for pollination, but nectaries are present and some pollen is carried from flower to flower by insects; bees seek out willows as the earliest source of nectar on warm spring days.

In detail, each male catkin (see page 115) consists of a dense cluster of small, very simple flowers. Each single flower is made up of a scale that is densely clad in white hairs, giving it a soft outline. Two stamens only spring up from the base of this scale, in contrast to the larger numbers found in the nearly-related poplars.

Female catkins (page 115) are also crowded, though each separate flower can be singled out. Each flower has a single bract and a long slender pistil, topped by two often bi-lobed stigmas. After pollination, the ovary develops into a seed pod, which splits from the top down to release numer-

PLATE CXXI
Winter twig of white willow (life size) and a single leaf bud ($\times$ 4). Note white down on bud.

ous fine seeds, bearing the white hairs that carry them on the wind. Willow seed is short-lived, and only those seeds that alight on damp, bare earth in midsummer are likely to produce seedlings. This explains why wild willows are nearly always seen along watersides, where moist mud is available, or else in places like gravel beds or rock crevices, where a seed can be blown into a damp, shaded spot. Once established they will thrive in any normal soil.

Willow seedlings are naturally very small. They bear first two tiny round seed leaves, then two little true leaves, oppositely set, then two larger leaves, also opposite; the alternate leaf arrangement then follows.

Willow wood is pale brown in colour, and exceptionally light in weight, though remarkably tough. In the slender twig form, or when split into thin bands, it is very pliable in the moist state, but sets into a firm shape as soon as it dries and seasons. For these reasons it is always the first choice for basket making. Other uses include cricket bats and artificial limbs, and, in the past, shoulder-yokes for dairymaids, so that they could carry two heavy pails of milk at one time.

The White willow, *Salix alba*, is the commonest of the timber tree species. It can be identified by the slender outline of its leaves, which are technically lanceolate (see page 112). They have a slightly toothed edge and are smooth on both surfaces. They are silvery-white below and greyish-green above; this whiteness, which gives the tree its name, is obvious and fascinating to watch when the wind stirs the foliage, as our photograph shows.

White willow is most often seen as a waterside tree in the English Midlands and southern counties, though its range extends to Scotland. Most of the quaint pollarded willows belong to this species (see page 116). They used to be cut over at intervals, and the slender shoots that arose were used for rough baskets and hurdle making.

Most of the weeping willows seen in gardens belong to a variety of this species, *Salix alba* variety *tristis*, though the true Weeping willow is *S. babylonica*; this has, in fact, been introduced from the neighbourhood of Babylon though it is also found in China, and is featured on the willow-pattern plate.

PLATE CXXII
Osier willow beds on Sedgemoor, Somerset. Summer.

PLATE CXXIII
White willow.

Salix alba variety coerulea Cricket-bat Willow

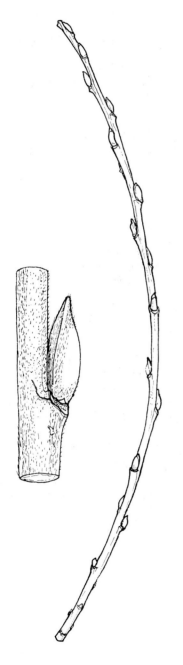

PLATE CXXIV
Winter twig of Cricket-bat willow
(life size) and a single leaf bud ($\times$ 8).

PLATE CXXV
Leafy shoot and female catkins of Cricket-bat willow in May
(life size). Left, a single pistil and two bi-lobed stigmas at its tip.
Right, leaf, lanceolate in shape, which is blue-green in colour and
bears silvery hairs on its lower surface.

Cricket-bat willow is a local variety of the White willow that probably arose as a wild tree in Essex, though today it can only be found in cultivation. It is always a female tree. The crown has a characteristic shape, a tapering pyramid or cone, and the foliage shows an attractive silvery-blue colour.

Willows are seldom raised from seed. Most kinds strike root readily from any stout twig pushed in the soil. Cricket-bat willow, the only kind grown commercially for timber today, is increased in this way. After one year's growth the rooted cuttings are lifted from the ground, cut back to a single stout bud, and then replanted in the nursery. The solitary bud grows up into a straight "set," and the "rooted sets" are then planted out on good agricultural land at a wide spacing, usually thirty feet apart.

Our photo shows a typical stand of Cricket-bat willows nearing maturity. Their lower branches have been pruned away to stop knots forming low down. After only twelve years of rapid growth the willows are felled. Their trunks are then cleft by hand tools such as axes and wedges, into several triangular "clefts," each a little larger than the finished blade of a bat. This blade is then shaped, again by hand, to its final form. The striking face of the blade must always lie along a radius of the growing tree—that is a line from the circumference to the centre.

PLATE CXXVI
Cricket-bat willows along a streamside; planted well apart on good farm land for bat production.

Salix caprea

Goat Willow

Goat willow is a familiar and widespread shrub found on the margins of ponds, lakes, streams, canals and rivers all over the British Isles (See p. 117). It often owes its survival as a wild tree to the inaccessibility of its natural seedbeds. Its tiny wind-borne seeds can sprout on a soft bog where animals cannot tread, or on a shingle bank or overhanging rock face that animals cannot reach. When it springs up on bare earth or gravel elsewhere it is very apt to be cropped back by a sharp-toothed sheep, cow or horse. Livestock find its leaves and young shoots palatable, and it is called Goat willow because goats readily browse it.

The leaves of goat willow are oval in outline, with well marked veins; they open early in the spring. The catkins are rounded and showy as they open before the leaves, in late March. They are often gathered for decoration. In many districts they are known as "palm," because they are sometimes used to ornament churches on Palm Sunday, instead of real eastern palm leaves. Authority for this can be found in the Book of Leviticus, chapter 23, verse 40: "And ye shall take on the first day the boughs of goodly trees, branches of palm trees, and the boughs of thick trees, and willows of the brook."

This Goat willow is typical of a group of similar shrubs found in various parts of Britain. Its twigs are rather brittle and it has no value for basketry, while it is always too small to be useful as timber. Gypsies, however, once made willow branchwood into clothes pegs.

Other shrub willows, such as the Common osier, *Salix viminalis*, have tough and supple branches and are cultivated to supply basket rods. The best willows for this purpose are, however, varieties of *S. triandra* which are always grown on the best agricultural soil, both well drained and well watered. Stools are established by setting out cuttings every 14 inches in rows 26 inches apart. Each year these stools send up clusters of very long thin shoots. These rods are cut off at the base in autumn, and the crop is renewed naturally by fresh shoots for several years before the stools and the soil are exhausted. The rods may be used just as gathered, as "brown willow," or else be stripped of their bark to give "white willow," or boiled with their bark on, before stripping, to give "buff willow," coloured by a natural dye in the bark. For fine work they are split into thin bands. They are woven when moist, and set firm as they dry.

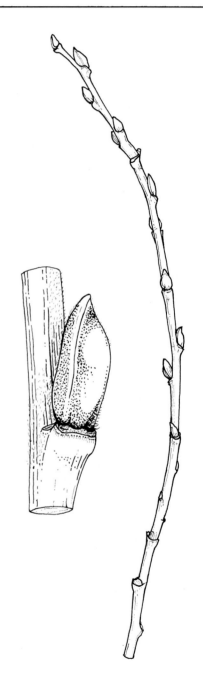

PLATE CXXVII
Winter twig of Goat willow, bearing leaf and shoot buds (life size), with a single bud (× 8).

Today, extensive willow beds can only be found around Langport on the moors of mid-Somerset (p. 110), but there are smaller ones in coastal districts, used mainly as sources of rods for fish traps and lobster pots. The photo on page 116 shows cut willow rods stacked to await bark-stripping, with their butts in a drain to keep them fresh and green. The lower photo on p. 117 illustrates cultivation.

PLATE CXXVIII
Winter twig of Goat willow, bearing the larger catkin buds, ready to burst into flower in spring (life size) with a single bud (× 5).

PLATE CXXX
Goat willows in full bloom. Left, flowering twig from female tree; right, flowering twig from male tree; both life-size.
Below, left, single male flower with hairy bract, two stamens, and basal nectary (× 10).
Below, right, single female flower, with hairy bract, stalked, two-stigmaed ovary, and basal nectary (× 10). Late March.

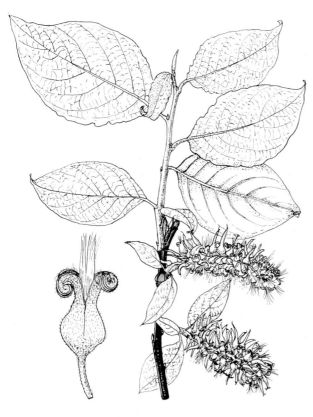

PLATE CXXXI
Leafy twig of female Goat willow bearing fruit in June (life size). Below, single stalked fruit pod splitting from above down and releasing hairy seeds.

PLATE CXXXII
Pollarded White willows, showing outgrowth by slender twigs from lopped upright stems. A familiar sight along Midland waterways.

PLATE CXXXIII
Osier growing in Somerset, spring. Foreground: Cut rods stacked along drainside prior to the peeling-off of their bark. Background: Pollard willows.

PLATE CXXXIV
Goat willow forms a shrubby tree growing in moist
hollows.

PLATE CXXXV
One-year-old osier bed grown from cuttings.

Salix fragilis   Crack Willow

This willow draws its odd name from a curious property of its twigs. If you bend them back they split off suddenly at the base, giving a sharp and clearly audible crack. This makes identification easy, but Crack willow can also be distinguished by the bright, smooth, orange-brown bark of the twigs, and its mid-green, slender leaves that lack the white down of the white willow. Crack willow forms a medium-sized tree that can often be found growing naturally along watersides. It is hardly ever planted, for its timber is brittle and useless, and it has few decorative merits.

Crack willows usually have a straggling much-branched crown like the tree illustrated, and this is apparently due to the frequent breakage of their twigs. But this strange feature has one advantage in the tree's struggle for survival, for every twig that breaks off is a natural cutting—twigs that get carried downstream often become stranded on mudbanks or stretches of shingle and take root there.

PLATE CXXXVI
Crack willow tree, showing typical, irregular, much-branched crown, well seen in winter.

Crack willow can therefore spread by detached twigs as well as by seed.

An odd feature of many streamside willows is that some of their roots grow in water, not in soil. You may see them as feathery pinkish clusters, trailing in the river, to gather both water and dissolved nutrients.

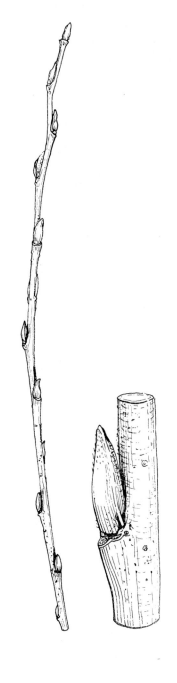

PLATE CXXXVII
Winter twig of male tree, with catkin buds (life size); single bud (× 6). Note tapering tip.

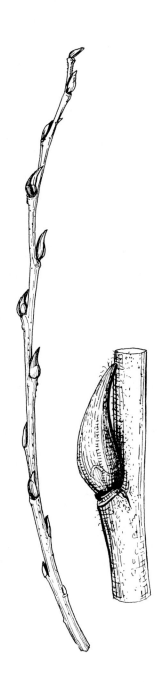

PLATE CXXXVIII
Winter twig of female tree, with catkin buds (life size); single ud (× 5). Note that female buds have blunt tips.

PLATE CXXXIX
Leafy twig of female crack willow, flowering in June ($\times \frac{2}{3}$).
Single female flower, consisting of hairy bract, two bi-lobed
stigmas, stalked ovary, and nectary ($\times$ 7).

PLATE CXL
Leafy twig of male crack willow, flowering in June ($\times \frac{3}{4}$).
Single male flower, consisting of hairy bract, two stamens, and
nectary ($\times$ 6).

Sorbus aucuparia

Rowan

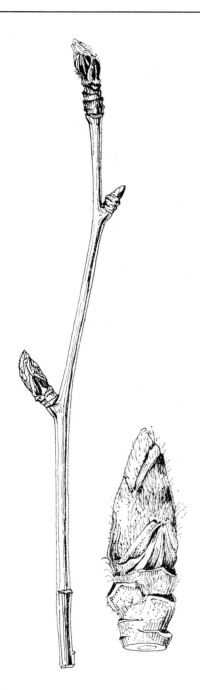

Rowan is widely planted as an ornamental tree in gardens and along roadsides, because of its unfailing display of white blossom in May and scarlet berries in September. It is also called the Mountain ash, because of its ash-like compound leaf, though the two trees have no other features in common.

Rowan belongs to the natural family *Rosaceae*, and the flowers show the structure typical of that group. Each individual blossom has five green sepals, five white petals, nectaries to attract bees, a large number of stamens, and a central pistil composed of three to four carpels. In this *Sorbus* genus, the fruit is a soft, fleshy berry, containing several small, hard seeds embedded in fleshy pulp. Another characteristic feature of the *Sorbus* genus is the grouping of the flowers, and their resultant fruits, in clusters that are made up of one main stalk and many smaller ones. Rowan berries are too sour to be eaten raw, but if sugar is added they can be made into a tasty jelly, used as a seasoning for game. See cover, which also shows foliage.

Rowan is typically a small tree with a smooth purplish-brown bark. Its winter buds are exceptionally large, dark purple in colour, and end in a peculiar one-sided point; each scale is tufted with white hairs. The leaves are pinnately compound, with about seven leaflets set on each side of the central stalk, which ends in a terminal leaflet. The leaflet edges are distinctly toothed; this feature, together with the fact that leaves and buds are *alternately set* on the twigs rather than opposite, enables one to tell the rowan apart from the ash tree quite easily.

Rowan berries are very attractive to birds, who swallow the small hard seeds along with the berries, and later void these seeds, often at a distance from the trees that grew them. This explains why rowans spring up naturally in odd inaccessible places, such as high rock faces, shingle banks, the ruins of old castles, and even in the forks of old decaying trees. Each seedling carries two small oval seed-leaves

PLATE CXLI
Winter twig of rowan, showing the exceptionally large buds with oblique points; they are dark purple in colour (life size). Right, a single bud about to burst; note hairy scale ($\times$ 3).

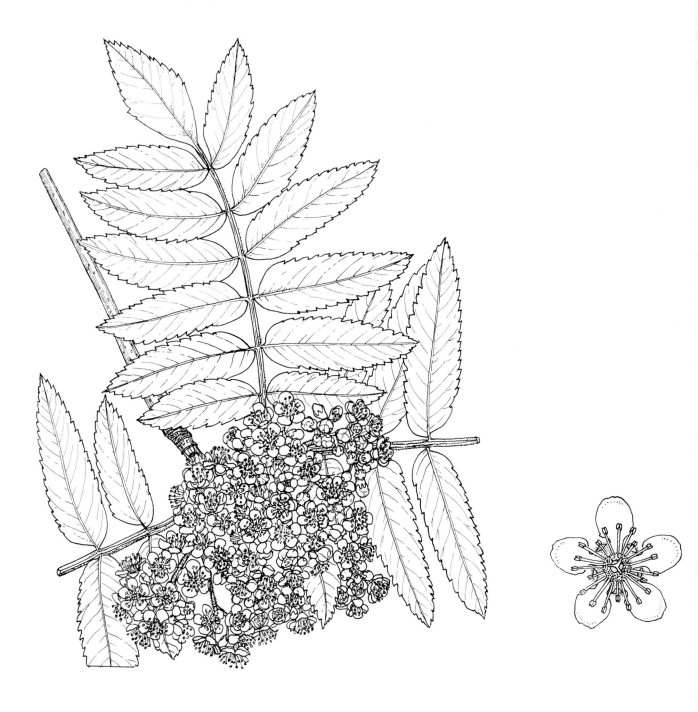

PLATE CXLII
Foliage and flower cluster of rowan; the compound leaves have toothed edges to their leaflets (life size).

PLATE CXLIII
Single rowan flower ($\times$ 4). There are five sepals, five petals, many stamens and a three-styled pistil.

PLATE CXLIV
Rowan berries and foliage (life size).

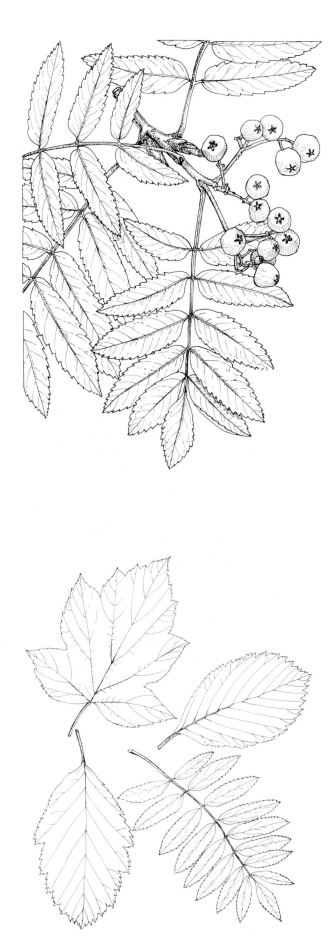

above the soil, followed by simple leaves and then compound ones. Under cultivation, the seed has to be stored for eighteen months in moist sand before it will sprout.

Rowan logs have a dark purplish-brown heartwood with a pale yellowish-brown sapwood layer around it. The wood is strong, hard, tough, and easily worked, but the tree is too small to yield supplies acceptable to industry. It was formerly used in country crafts for furniture, tool handles, mallet heads, cart shafts, bowls and platters, and household utensils such as spinning wheels.

Rowan is very hardy and is found as far up the hills as any other tree, often in rocky clefts where grazing sheep cannot destroy the seedling or sapling tree. It was widely planted in the Scottish Highlands because of a curious though widespread belief that it would protect dwellings from witchcraft. It often survives amid the ruins of long-deserted crofting settlements, making it easier to spot them on the lonely hill. The Gaelic name for this tree is *caorunn*, and the Welsh, *cerddin*. We draw the name "rowan" from the old Norse *røn*. This is linked with the word "rune," for the Norsemen carved their runic alphabet on tablets cleft from rowan wood, as well as on stone. They did this with a sharp tool called a *reiss*, and today some foresters still use a *race* to carve reference numbers and measured dimensions on the ends of logs. The genus *Sorbus* includes two other distinct trees that grow wild in Britain, and there are also a number of intermediate kinds that probably arise through these two kinds interbreeding with the rowan, or with each other. The Common whitebeam, *Sorbus aria*, which grows on chalk and limestone soils, has green buds and simple, oval leaves with toothed edges and very conspicuous white undersides, clad in downy hairs. An intermediate race, called the Swedish whitebeam or *Sorbus intermedia*, has pinnately lobed leaves with toothed edges; it is common in north-east Scotland, where it may arise from seeds brought from Scandinavia by immigrating birds.

The Wild Service Tree, *Sorbus torminalis*, which is found as a rarity in southern England and South Wales, has palmately lobed leaves—rather like those of a maple, and brown berries that are just sweet enough to eat. The name "Service" comes from Latin *cerevisia* meaning "beer," because the berries of a related tree were used to sweeten that drink. The leaf forms of the four mentioned species of *Sorbus* are shown here.

PLATE CXLVI
Rowan in blossom; it is typically a small much-branched
tree, springing from seeds dropped by birds in hedgerows or on
waste land.

Tilia europaea   Common Lime

The Common lime tree is believed to be a natural hybrid between two wild kinds that are rare in Britain, though frequent on the Continent. One of these is the Broad-leaved lime, *Tilia platyphyllos*, and the other is the Small-leaved lime, *T. cordata*. Native limes can be found growing wild in a few rocky woods along the Welsh Borders, in the Lake District and in Yorkshire, but only in spots where their seedlings have escaped the busy teeth of sheep. Common lime is usually cultivated, being increased by cuttings. Lime seeds lie dormant for eighteen months after ripening, and then produce a pair of oddly-shaped seed-leaves, lobed like the fingers of a hand, followed by normal foliage.

All the lime trees of the *Tilia* genus have features that make its identification easy. Every bud shows exactly two scales on its outer surface, one being larger than the other, rather like a finger and thumb. Buds and leaves are alternately set on rather zig-zag twigs which are often tinged crimson above. Leaves are shaped like a conventional heart, and are sometimes slightly oblique, at the base. They are long-stalked, soft-textured and pale green, with toothed edges.

Flowers are borne in July, in bunches on long stalks that have a very peculiar feature—a large oblong leafly bract attached to the stalk for half its length. Each separate bloom stands on an individual stalk and has five green sepals, five yellowish-white petals, a large number of stamens and a one-chambered ovary that bears 5 stigmas on a single style.

Pollination is done by insects, and beekeepers regard lime trees as a rich source of nectar and hence of honey. On the Continent the flowers are dried and used to make a fragrant and refreshing tea. Each flower ripens, by September, a nut-like fruit which is grey, round and hard, and holds a single seed.

Lime wood is pale yellowish-cream in colour, with no obvious grain or figure. It is moderately hard, works to a smooth finish, and is very stable when seasoned. This fits it for a few exacting uses, such as piano keys, hat blocks, shoe lasts, and decorative carving. It was used, in the seventeenth century, by Grinling Gibbons for his masterpieces of wood sculpture.

Limes are no longer grown commercially, and the small amount of timber used comes from ornamental trees. They are widely planted in streets, parks and gardens for their

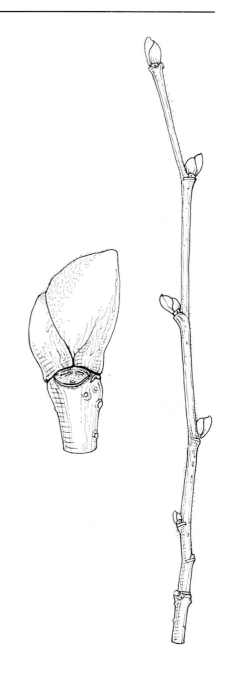

PLATE CXLVII
Winter twig of lime, with rounded buds set alternately on somewhat zig-zag twigs (life size). Right, single bud, showing only two outer scales, in a "finger-and-thumb" pattern ($\times$ 4).

pleasing foliage. Limes tolerate a severe degree of pruning, but some strains form bushy outgrowths of twigs at the base of the trunk.

Lime bark is pale grey and smooth. Its fibres are so strong that they were once used for ropes, and gardeners still occasionally employ it for binding up bundles of plants. It is called "bass" or "bast," and in America the wood of the lime is known as "basswood." The lime is also known, on both sides of the Atlantic by its older name of "linden."

A fine lime tree appears in our cover picture.

The tallest broadleaved tree in Britain is a lime in Duncombe Park, close to Helmsley in Yorkshire, which scales 154 feet. The stoutest recorded lime stands at Cobham Hall in Kent, and is 38 feet round.

PLATE CXLVIII
Lime foliage and flowers in July, life size. Leaves are long-stalked and heart-shaped, and some have an oblique base. Flowers are carried in clusters on a long stalk with a leafy bract attached. Single flower (below × 5) has five sepals, many stamens and a pistil tipped with 5 stigmas.

PLATE CXLIX
Lime seedling, showing the seed leaves with finger-like lobes (× ½).

PLATE CL
Foliage and ripening fruits of lime in September (× ⅔).

127

PLATE CLI
An open-grown lime tree in summer foliage. Note the "browsing level", below which cattle bite off all foliage.

Ulmus glabra   Wych Elm

The elms are a very distinct genus of trees which includes a wide variety of forms or varieties. Few experts agree about the correct ranking of many of these, as will be discussed later on page 134, but there is no dispute at all over the status and identification of the Wych elm. This is a native species found all over the British Isles, with old-established names in Gaelic—*leamhan* (pronounced "leven") and in Welsh—*llwyfan*.

Characters that it shares with all the elms include rounded winter buds, set alternately along the twigs, and simple oval leaves with one very odd feature. Elm leaves are always more or less lop-sided; the two halves may be obviously uneven, or else the base may be oblique. The leaf edges are doubly toothed, and veins are distinct. Elm flowers appear early in the spring, in late February or early March, well before the leaves. These flowers are usually seen high in the crowns of tall trees, as purplish red tufts on bare branches. They arise in clusters, each holding several small simple blossoms. Each separate flower has five sepals, five stamens with purplish-red anthers, and a two-styled pistil. Pollination is effected by the wind, and there are no petals and no nectaries to attract insects.

After pollination the calyx and stamens fall away, and each pistil ripens a single seed, set at or near the centre of a yellowish-green papery wing. The clusters of winged seeds ripen in early May, just before, or just after, the elm has expanded its leaves. They are quite showy and are sometimes mistaken for flowers. Few seeds are fertile. The good ones germinate within a few weeks of falling, and send up two seed-leaves, followed by a pair of oppositely-set, symmetrical juvenile leaves; the normal adult leaves—alternately set and lop-sided—follow.

The heartwood of all the elms is a rich warm reddish brown in colour; around it there grows a thin band of pale-yellow sapwood, surrounded in turn by rough grey bark. Elm timber always has a lively figure caused by the varying sizes of the vessels or pores in each annual ring. Those pores that are formed first in spring, and so lie nearest the centre of the tree, are largest; smaller ones succeed them in an irregular, stepped, pattern. The grain of elm timber is interlocked in a remarkable way that makes it almost impossible to split. It is hard, strong, yet easily worked with cutting tools, though not with splitting tools.

Large quantities are used for furniture and coffin boards, and for making strong packing cases for heavy machinery. Elm is also employed for the side planking of sheds and summerhouses, often as "waney-edged" boards in a rustic pattern. Because it is so hard to split, it is used for chair seats, since it does not break when legs and uprights are driven in; also for wheel-hubs, because it will not split when the spokes are driven home. Mallet heads are another use. In dock and harbour work large elm planks and beams are used where resistance to abrasion—by shingle or by vessels, is essential.

Craft uses of elm wood include water pipes and water pumps, which were made of wood before metal-working was developed. When kept continually wet it does not perish, and disused pipes 200-years old, still quite sound, are often dug up in London. But it is not durable at ground level—where both air and moisture are present to encourage wood-rotting fungi, so it should never be used for fencing.

Most kinds of elm readily send up *suckers*, which are shoots that arise from their underground roots, and may eventually develop into trees. But Wych elm is an exception; it will not sucker and can only be increased by seed.

The distinguishing features of the Wych elm include stout twigs, large winter buds, and a remarkably large leaf, usually three to six inches long, which has markedly rough or scabrid surfaces. Wych elm bark is regularly patterned; the trunk often carries an open network of ribs and furrows. The trunk always tends to branch low down, as our photo shows, giving rise to a number of spreading ascending branches, which eventually droop at their tips to make a dome-shaped crown. The seeds are large, and are set in the centre of big wings.

Wych elm, which is also called Scots elm and mountain elm because it is the only common kind in the North, is usually found growing as a wild tree in Highland glens or upland valleys. It is also planted as a park tree, particularly in Scottish cities where it thrives despite smoke, poor soil, and a cool climate. Wych elms, intended partly for timber and partly for shelter and landscape effect, can be found on many private estates throughout Britain, more often in mixed woods than as pure stands. Wych elm timber is considered to be somewhat stronger and more easily

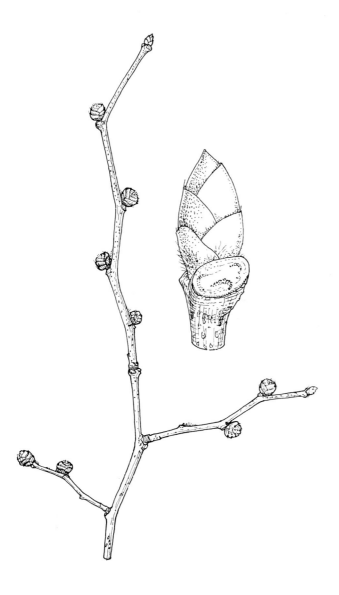

PLATE CLII
Winter twig of Wych elm, showing the stout twigs, large rounded flower buds and smaller growth buds (life size). Single growth bud (× 6).

worked than that of other elms; it has specialised uses in boat building and carriage building, but most of it goes for furniture. The word "wych" originally meant "pliant" or "supple," but was often applied, in the past, to mean "elm tree," regardless of species.

Wych elm flowers are illustrated on page 138, seeds here, and leaves on page 139.

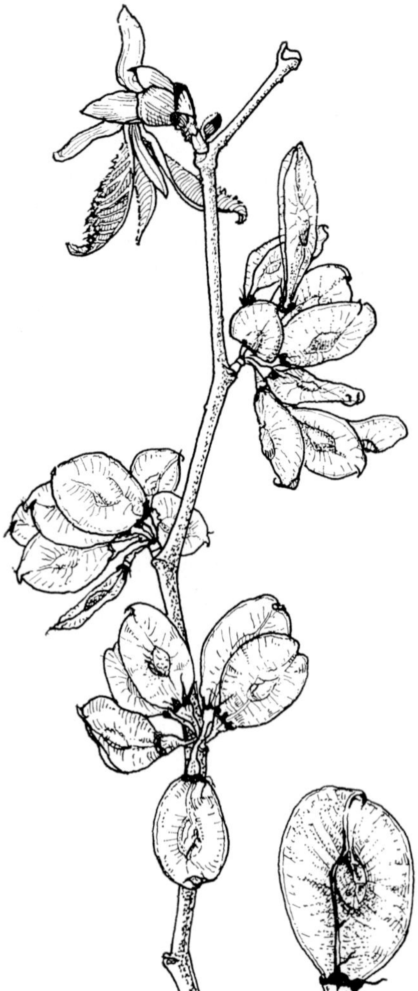

PLATE CLIII
Fruiting twig of Wych elm in May showing the large winged seed; leaf-buds just breaking. (life size)—single seed (× 6).

PLATE CLIV
Wych elm, showing characteristic branching and the domed
crown of an open-grown tree.

Ulmus hollandica variety vegeta

Huntingdon Elm

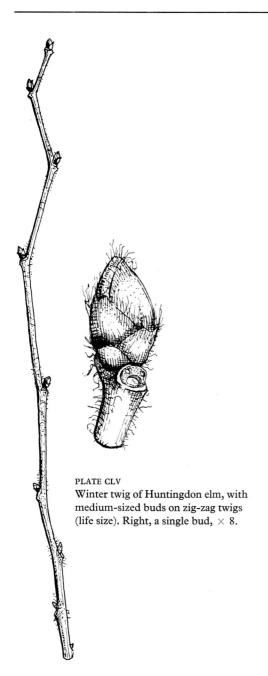

This beautiful tree is one of the many regional forms of elm that puzzle the botanists, but simply delight lovers of the English landscape. It is believed to be a natural hybrid between the Wych elm, *Ulmus glabra*, and the Smooth-leaved elm, *U. carpinifolia*. It forms a magnificent tree with a straight bole and long straight branches, usually ascending. The leaves are large, like those of the Wych elm, and are remarkably oblique at the base. Distinguishing features are reddish hairs in the vein arches of the under surface, and a *slight* hairiness of the upper surface.

Huntingdon elm draws its name from its discovery in a nursery at Huntingdon, about the year 1750.

The nurseryman concerned propagated and sold it so extensively that it became prominent along the hedgerows of Huntingdonshire and neighbouring counties, and today many fine specimens can be seen elsewhere.

Unlike the Wych elm, it sends up sucker shoots freely. As our illustrations show, its characters of bud, leaf, flower and seed fall somewhere between the Wych elm and the English elm, described on the following pages. Flowers are shown on page 138, seeds on this page, leaves on page 139, outline on page 141.

PLATE CLV
Winter twig of Huntingdon elm, with medium-sized buds on zig-zag twigs (life size). Right, a single bud, × 8.

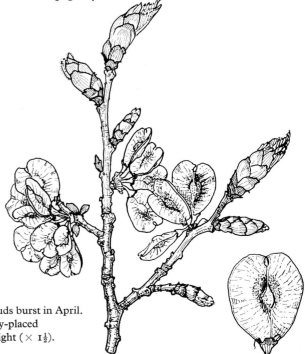

PLATE CLVI
Fruits of Huntingdon elm, ripening as the leaf-buds burst in April. Each fruit has a large wing with a single, centrally-placed seed, as shown by the enlarged example on the right ($\times 1\frac{1}{2}$).

PLATE CLVII

English elm. The single erect trunk contrasts with the
spreading crown of the Wych elm, though many branches
are ascending.

Ulmus procera English Elm

The English elm is the finest of several varied forms that can be found across the lowland plains of Southern England and the Midlands. As a group they are called "Field elms" because they are usually seen in hedgerows between fertile agricultural fields. The causes of their variability still puzzle the experts. One possibility is the natural spread of certain Continental elms to south-east England while the land bridge with France still existed. These European species, which are themselves variable, may later have spread slowly north and west, hybridizing between themselves and with the well-established native Wych elm, to give local races. Another theory is that certain kinds were deliberately brought over by Roman, Anglo-Saxon or Norman settlers, to provide timber and also fodder for livestock. In some Eastern countries elms are lopped annually as a source of cattle food, and goat-keepers still make occasional use of elm foliage even in Britain.

As a rule, the seed of these lowland Field elms has only a low degree of fertility, if any. In practice they are increased by separating sucker shoots from their parent roots, by layering branches, or by grafting. This means that any peculiar kind of elm is reproduced exactly, as a "clone" or "cultivar." Identification by means of small specimens, such as a few leaves or shoots, is difficult, because elm leaves vary a great deal in shape, size, and hairiness, even on the same tree. Leaves from vigorous sucker shoots, for example, are usually far larger than others, and may be a different shape. But when the whole tree is seen it is often possible to assign it to a particular sort, as its habit of growth will aid the impressions given by the smaller portions. The illustration on page 141 shows characteristic crown patterns for a few common kinds.

These Lowland or Field elms are rarely found growing wild, or even in pure woods established artificially. They nearly always grow along hedgerows, or else in small spinneys or on patches of rough ground where hedgerows meet. The network of hedges that runs right across the landscape is artificial in origin, having been formed during the great Enclosure Movement, largely in the eighteenth century. A high proportion of the elms we see today are descended, as suckers, from the trees planted by the landowners and farmers who made the original enclosures. These parent

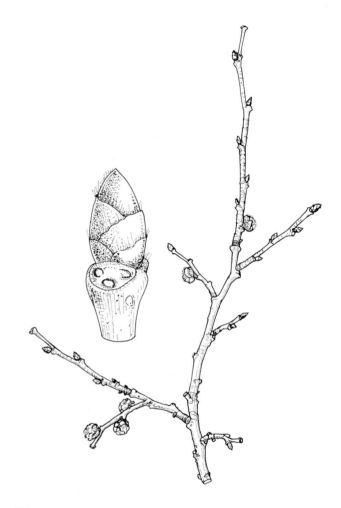

PLATE CLVIII
Winter twig of English elm, showing fine branching, and small growth buds with larger flower buds (× ⅔). Single bud (× 6).

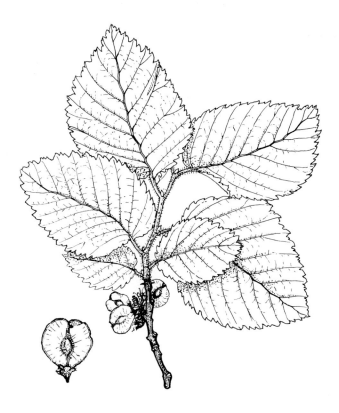

PLATE CLIX
Leafy twig of English elm, with typical hairy surfaces, and
small, randomly set leaves; note the small fruits (life size).
Single fruit (× 2½).

elms were often set out at the same time as the first haw-
thorn bushes that made up the hedges.

John Evelyn, who is regarded as the father of British
forestry, described five methods of propagating elms by
vegetative means in his *Silva*, published in 1664. Further
details were contributed by Alexander Hunter in his 1776
edition of the same book. These authors make it clear
that the large-scale raising of elms, from foundation stocks
maintained by nurserymen, was a well established practice from about 1625 to 1775; later records show that it was
continued for a further 100 years. This explains why the
elms in a particular district often look remarkably similar—
they came from the same nursery and the same parent
stock. It also accounts for the occasional appearance of a
few "unusual" elms in a particular place, since planting or
propagating material could readily be sent over long dis-
tances. Landowners with two or more estates—a common
situation, would often use their best available elm on both.
One landowner, "Planter John," Duke of Montagu (died
1749), planted 72 miles of elm avenues across Northamp-
tonshire.

The English elm is usually given specific status, as *Ulmus
procera* Salisbury. There is no elm quite like it on the Continent; in fact this, and a few other peculiar regional elms,
are the only trees unique to Britain.

English elm can be found over most of the English midlands, alone or in association with other kinds. The Severn
valley is its stronghold and it may have arisen there.

The twigs of English elm are hairy and slender, with a
typically zig-zag habit of growth; the buds, which are also
hairy, are small. The leaves are small and oval, and have a
roughly hairy upper surface. Seeds and wings are likewise
distinctly smaller than those of Wych elm. The bark on the
trunk is thick and furrowed into ridges. Suckers spring up
abundantly from the roots of old trees, but seed is rarely
fertile. Suckers that spring up in fields are either eaten up
by livestock or cut up by ploughs; only those that come up
along the hedge itself can survive.

English elm has a magnificent habit of growth, which
cannot be matched elsewhere; it adds an individual note
to the landscapes of England's vales. The trunk is stout

135

and erect, growing far taller than any associated tree, and from it there extend great billowing clouds of foliage, borne on distinct branch groups. Growth is rapid, and elms are rightly planted, preserved, or encouraged to grow from suckers along the hedgerows as a profitable source of timber. Records for height are 141 feet, and for girth 25 feet, though today no tree taller than 122 feet can be found, this stands at Youngsbury near Ware in Hertfordshire. Propagation today is usually effected by using softwood cuttings, using mist in summer.

Between 1930 and 1960 all our elms were seriously threatened by the Dutch Elm disease, caused by the fungus *Cerotocystis ulmi*: which is carried from tree to tree by the little Elm bark beetle, *Scolytus scolytus*. This spread rapidly at first, but the surviving elms appear resistant to it. Unfor-tunately another serious outbreak occurred in 1970, and this has led to the recommendation that only resistant strains of elms should be used for future planting. Huntingdon elm is the most resistant native kind; but the Dutch-bred Commelin elm is the safest available kind to plant.

Ordinary elms should not be planted in places such as parks that are much frequented by the public, since they are apt—though only occasionally—to shed large branches without warning. Narrow-crowned elms, such as the Cornish elm, described on the following pages, are free from this danger.

Flowers of English elm are illustrated on page 138, seeds on page 135, and leaves on page 139. A well-grown tree appears on our front cover.

PLATE CLX
English elms, showing typical domed crowns of foliage, and
large rounded groups of side branches.

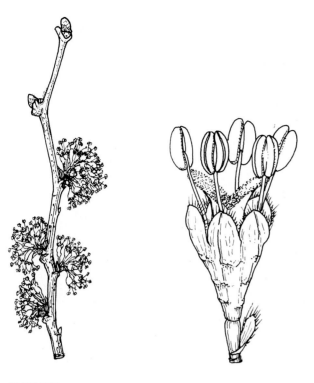

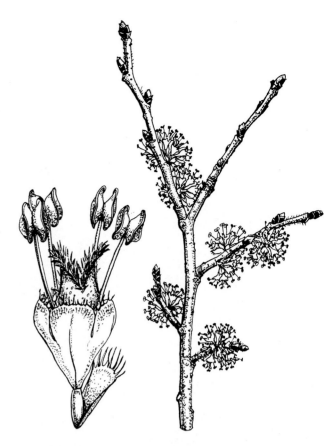

PLATE CLXI

Flowering twig of Wych elm in March (life size). Single flower ($\times$ 7) showing basal bract, calyx of five sepals, five stamens, and two-styled pistil.

PLATE CLXII

Flowering twig of Huntingdon elm ($\times$ ¾). Single flower ($\times$ 7), with stamens at a late stage.

PLATE CLXIII

Flowering twig of English elm (life size). Single flower ($\times$ 7) showing, in this example, only four stamens.

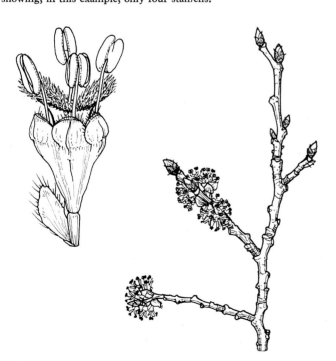

PLATE CLXIV

Typical leaves of three sorts of elm, all life size. Top: English elm, hairy all over on lower surface. Left: Huntingdon elm, showing reddish hairs in "vein arches" of lower surface; slightly hairy on upper surface. Right: Wych elm, rough (scabrid) to the touch on both surfaces.

Ulmus carpinifolia variety cornubiensis   Cornish Elm

Cornish elm is one of several regional races of the smooth-leaved elm, *Ulmus carpinifolia*, that have remarkably narrow crowns. In this form the lower branches are more or less fastigiate, following the upward trend of the trunk and not diverging far nor growing very large. Towards the tip larger branches spread out at a sharp angle, rather like the inner ribs of an umbrella, to carry a rounded crown. Because their branching is light, certain narrow-crowned kinds are often chosen for street or park planting, since the danger from branch-shedding is small. The leaves are small and oval.

Elms of this growth habit are common in Cornwall and West Devon where they add a characteristic note to the scenery. Other forms, such as the Jersey or Wheatley elm, *Ulmus carpinifolia* var. *sarniensis* Rehd., are common in the Channel Islands. Elms are remarkably resistant to salt winds off the sea, and they flourish on the exposed cliffs of Cornwall, Jersey and Guernsey where other tall trees are blighted. Thickets and hedgerow trees are renewed by abundant sucker shoots.

PLATE CLXV
Cornish elms.

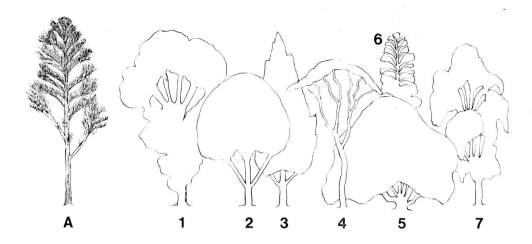

PLATE CLXVI

Typical elm crowns: A. Cornish elm, *Ulmus carpinifolia* variety *cornubiensis;* 1. English elm, *U procera;* 2. Huntingdon elm, *U × hollandica* variety *vegetata;* 3. Wheatley elm, *U carpinifolia* variety *sarniensis;* 4. Dutch elm, *U × hollandica;* 5. Wych elm, *U glabra;* 6. Cornish elm, *U carpinifolia* variety *cornubiensis;* 7. Smooth-leaved elm, *U carpinifolia*

INDEX

Note. The scientific name of each species, *in italics*, is followed by the name or initial of the botanist who is the authority for that name; "L." stands for the Swedish botanist Linnaeus. The botanical family is shown, within brackets, at the first mention of each genus.

Printed in England for Her Majesty's Stationery Office by Wells KPL Swindon Press, Swindon, Wilts.

Dd 505962 K104 2/73